NORTH END BOY

INNOCENCE AND EXPERIENCE AMID THE SEVEN WONDERS OF ELIZABETH, NEW JERSEY

Kevin P. Brady

Printed in the United States.

ISBN 978-1-7378161-0-2 Paperback
ISBN 978-1-7378161-1-9 Ebook

Introduction

This is a book about a not-so-distant time in America when most people still worked with their hands. Make it 1978 – a rip in time before computers, cell phones and social media. The most complicated piece of personal technology was the automobile sitting in the driveway, something guys could fix in a pinch by themselves.

In 1978, the United States was reeling from rising crime, race riots, gas lines, a devalued dollar, an indifferent stock market, a generation gap and the self-doubt brought on by a lost war in Vietnam. The country endured high unemployment and even higher inflation, a condition most economists considered impossible. Yet there it was. Mortgage rates topped out at eighteen percent. Stiff foreign competition forced the closure of large-scale manufacturing sites and decimated the trade unions. Newly aggressive Communist foes challenged a crippled America and threatened to re-write the ending to World War II. All under the imminent threat of a nuclear holocaust.

It was a worrisome time to come of age.

There were, however, some consolations. There was less

money around then — but there was less to spend it on. The faithful filled up their churches and synagogues. Divorce was rare. Extended families provided deep reserves of security. Nobody questioned the viability of American political institutions. This is not to say that people were happier then. They weren't. Only that churches, families and government provided a stable home front against a changing and often hostile outside world.

This is the story of seven friends in their early twenties who, over a thirty-six hour period, sort out their destiny against a backdrop of urban crime, abandoned factories and political corruption in 1978. These were my friends.

I could not do justice to my friends without a description of the local businesses that formed them: Singers Sewing Machine Works, Burry Biscuits, the Bayway Refinery. Without the economic draw of these big employers, most would have been born somewhere else and my story would be different. Nor would my story be complete without mentioning the churches, the cops, the politicians and the mob – each of which exerted their own gravitational pull upon us.

My tale is told in Elizabeth, New Jersey, where I was born and raised. Much of the action takes place in the North End, where my Irish immigrant parents settled after the war. An intensely local book, *North End Boy* is also a larger meditation on post-war America, as seen through the eyes of a young man with immigrant sensibilities and working-class roots.

At least that's how it looked to me.

Cranford, New Jersey
July 2, 2021

Dedication

To my wife, Maureen, for more reasons
than could possibly be listed here.

To her brother, Jack Cashill, who provided deep
emotional support and professional editorial
guidance in the writing of this book.

To Joe Traynor, who kept a sharp eye on the artistic
and commercial potential of this project.

To Dave Wiener, my best critic.

To my immediate and extended family, who have supported
all of my ventures, both the inspired and the foolish ones.
With a special shout-out to my sister, Veronica, who helped
secure the images used in the book.

To the Alers: Eddie, Billy, Timbo, Keith, Raymond, Paul,
Frank, Bobby, Tim, Brian, Tommy, Colin, Peter, Chris and
Higbo – for a lifetime of laughs.

CHAPTER 1

The Courthouse

"How about a ride, Joe?" – Butch Mahon

"Get bent." – Joe Ball

Patrolman Joe Ball stopped at the light across the street from the courthouse. He looked up at the stately white building gleaming in the morning light, where punishment and mercy fell on the just and the unjust alike. He had been there many times in the course of his official duties — once to the 17th floor, where he took in the view of the entire city. To the north, Newark Airport and the Burry Biscuit factory, which alone covered five city blocks. To the south, the Bayway Refinery and next to it the Goethals Bridge, which connected his city to the Isle of Staten. To the east and straight down Elizabeth Avenue, the New Jersey Turnpike and the massive Singer factory, purveyor of sewing machines to the world and almost a city in itself. Together, they made up the seven wonders of Elizabeth, New Jersey.

But none of them impressed Joe Ball, who patrolled the ethnic neighborhoods that lay among the seven wonders: Polish Bayway under the bridge, Italian Peterstown north of the refinery, the Cubans who fled Castro to settle on Elizabeth Avenue under the Turnpike, the more recent Black and Hispanic immigrants who battled it out in the shadow of the great sewing machine works, the polyglot North End between the airport and giant biscuit factory.

Joe made it his business to know each of these tribes and the streets that defined them. He knew the Polish refinery workers, the DeCavalcante family, who ran the rackets out of Peterstown, the cops in the North End, the shop owners on Elizabeth Avenue, drug dealers everywhere. After twenty years on the job, Joe had deliberately chosen not to rise within the ranks, preferring instead to work the streets as a lowly patrolman. His beat covered the bars, the gambling dens, the cat houses, and anything else in need of protection. Cops who knew and saw such things could be paid *not* to see and know them. And patrolman Joe Ball saw everything.

Joe was off-duty, on his way home from a card game run by the DeCavalcante's, where he provided the muscle. About fifty, stoutly built and bullet-headed, he looked every inch the veteran non-com that he was. At the age of eighteen, Joe had volunteered and served with the Third Army in Patton's madcap dash across Europe. Like many survivors, Joe never discussed the war. He kept a Bronze Star and a Purple Heart hidden in a cigar box at the back of his bedroom drawer. The war and the peace that followed left indelible marks on the young person of Joe Ball. The war sharpened him. The peace gave him confidence — and for good reason.

Immediately after the war, the United States accounted for 50 percent of world GNP, three times the size of the combined Axis powers and four times the size of the Soviet Union. The U.S. owned 66 percent of the world's productive capacity and 70 percent of all automobiles. Los Angeles had more cars than Asia. Americans owned 80 percent of all electrical appliances on earth. With only five percent of the world population, Americans possessed more wealth than 95 percent of the rest of the world. The U.S. dollar was the only reserve currency worth holding. Americans had won, and they had won big. War reparations? Why bother?

As the last men standing far above a war-ravaged globe, it seemed pretty clear to American leaders that the whole place needed to be re-built. With a peace dividend burning a hole in their pocket, can-do Americans set about re-constructing the world in the only way they could: in their own image and likeness. The Marshall Plan created democratic Mini-Me's in Europe and Japan — but not the Soviet Union, which had its own notions about the pursuit of happiness.

By 1978, however, deep questions began to trouble the likes of Joe Ball. A stalemate in Korea, two Kennedy assassinations, the killing of Martin Luther King, a humiliating loss in Vietnam, a generation gap, race riots, a Nixonian landslide followed by a Nixonian collapse, high interest rates, dollar devaluation, gas lines, stagflation, an indifferent stock market, rising crime – all these conspired to shake the confidence of the greatest generation. Newly aggressive

3

Communist foes challenged a crippled America and threatened to re-write the ending to World War II. Freedom itself seemed to be losing out to a new breed of totalitarians who controlled more and more of the earth's surface. Thus came doubt into the mind of patrolman Joe Ball. Traffic was unusually light for 9:00 in the morning at the corner of Broad Street and Elizabeth Avenue, the Times Square of the city. So when an unlikely kid in a brilliant, brand new, red '78 Cadillac stopped next to him, Joe rolled up for a closer look. He leaned over and immediately recognized Butch Mahon through the sealed windows of the air-conditioned Caddy.

Butch was an unpleasant piece of business. Although he went to St. Catherine's School with Joe's kids in the North End, he really belonged in reform school, if there. He managed to hang in because his mother worked BINGO, fairs, and a million other odd jobs that kept the place going. The twenty-five-cent seat money and single dollar that each family dropped into the collection basket helped, but the volunteers, both lay and clerical, formed the beating heart of the parish. It took all of them to preserve Butch's shot at redemption.

In addition to the parish, the archdiocese of Newark, and arguably the Pope, all of whom were fighting to save the soul of Butch Mahon, there were a number of secular authorities trying to salvage his *civic* life. As a resident of the over-governed state of New Jersey, Butch frequently tangled with all the branches of city, county, state, and federal law enforcement, none of which had any measurable effect on his distinctly uncivil behavior. Despite the combined efforts of church and state, Butch could not avoid his destiny as a low-level thug. Butch, the delinquent youth, turned into Butch, the felon, with the inevitability of the seasons. After eight difficult years in parochial grammar school, the Dominican nuns released Butch into the greater wilds of Elizabeth with a mixture of relief, concern, and a healthy measure of old-fashioned Catholic guilt at having failed young Butch.

Joe tapped the horn of his '71 Chevy and got Butch's attention. Butch scowled even when asleep. Aroused, his rubbery face twisted this way and that, following the erratic impulses of his overwrought brain. On recognizing patrolman Joe Ball, his dull narrow eyes opened wide in fear. He considered making a run for it. His mind bounced between the animal poles of flight and fight. The Cadillac was, of course, stolen, and the brief, violent, pointless life of Butch Mahon passed before him. He gripped the steering wheel and prepared to floor the Caddy. He was sure he could outrun and outweave Joe's Chevy through the downtown streets of Elizabeth. Old Joe Ball might not even chase him. Joe stuck his hand out and casually signaled for Butch to roll down his window.

"Running a few errands, Butch?" asked Joe.

"No, Mr. Ball, I mean Officer Ball. No," stammered Butch.

"Pull over and get in."

Butch turned right onto Broad St. and parked the Caddy. Something in the calm demeanor of the street cop, something in the easy way he motioned for Butch to pull over, re-assured

Butch and told him that he should not run, that there was another way.

"Where are you taking the Caddy?" asked Joe.

The question implied what they both knew. At twenty-three, Butch was too old to be joy riding around town at nine o'clock on a Friday morning. This was business. The car was destined for a chop shop, where it would be cut into a hundred pieces within the hour and dispatched into the aftermarket. The only question was where.

"North End."

"McClellan Street?"

"Yeah."

"Let's go."

"You're coming with me?"

"Yeah, I know them."

Butch relaxed. Joe Ball knew the chop shop and that seemed to be a good thing, a safe thing. Joe would even escort him to his destination. Butch got back into the Cadillac and slowly cruised down Broad Street, under the railroad arch and onto the familiar streets of the North End. They stopped at the red light on North Avenue. Both looked up and to the left at the flashing sign over the bank to check the time, a ritual for everyone who passed this way:

9:15

July 21

90 degrees

The bank clock didn't convey the humidity, about 90 percent. Nor did it convey the sensation of breathing in the used-up industrial exhaust of Elizabeth at the height of summer. Across the street on Newark Avenue, the day shift had begun at the Burry Biscuit factory. The sickly-sweet aroma of strawberry Scooter Pies (universally reviled in the North End) further thickened up the ozone.

As they drove, Patrolman Joe Ball considered his options. He had Butch dead to rights. He could let Butch go and receive a deposit in his favor bank, a small deposit from a bit player destined for prison, which was worth almost nothing. Or he could play out this little drama and possibly get a larger deposit from the chop shop, maybe even a little cash. And who knew what might come after that? More dangerous, perhaps, but probably worth it. He didn't really know the guys who ran the chop shop — but what of it?

The favor bank was real cop stuff, something deeply embedded in the job, closer to their blue hearts than the right to overtime or funded pensions. All cops kept track of favors given and favors received from fellow cops. Every cop stored up these favors in his private account and knew exactly what every other cop in the world owed him. The favor bank issued unprinted currency for cops, currency that could only be spent by cops on other cops. But the favor bank was more real, and probably more valuable, than legal tender. It also provided a backup system of justice when the everyday system up in the courthouse failed, and so helped to keep the earth from spinning off its axis. The difference between the favor bank of Joe Ball and that of other cops was that Joe extended credit to criminals.

Joe followed the Caddy to a gas station, which was unusually busy. The garage door opened and both cars entered. Joe and Butch got out of their cars, and the door came down behind them.

"Who are *you*?" said a worker, who looked Joe up and down and detected the cop lurking beneath the plain clothes.

"Where's the owner?" said Joe.

"Inside," said the worker, with a nod to the office.

Joe walked into the office. The walls were covered with girly calendars from the previous ten years. The desk was piled high with neglected customer invoices from the same period, a sure sign of an all cash business.

"I ran into a friend on my way home, the guy who brought in the Caddy," said Joe. "I made sure he got here okay."

"Thanks," said the owner, who reached into his pocket, peeled off $ 300 from his wad and handed it to Joe. "For your trouble."

"No trouble."

"No more after this, right?" said the owner, who still held onto his end of the cash.

"No more."

The owner released the bills, and Joe slipped them into his pocket. An understanding had been reached. The money was a tip for services rendered, not the prelude to a larger shakedown. Joe would stay quiet, and the owner would go about his business of relieving traffic on the streets of Elizabeth, presumably under the protection of someone further up the chain. The peace would hold.

Out in the garage, Butch realized he was miles away from home and his ride was about to be sold for parts, a thought that had not occurred to him when he drove in. Flush with cash and feeling good about his recent caper with Joe Ball, an obvious solution presented itself to Butch.

"How about a ride, Joe?"

"Get bent."

Joe decided he needed some sleep, so he headed back to his home just a short drive away on Sheridan Avenue. His wife sat at the kitchen table reading The *Daily Journal*, chronicler of all things Elizabeth. She looked up at him, placed her finger on the paper to hold her spot, and greeted him from behind her reading glasses. Their boys were stirring, each of them in various stages of morning, noon, or night, depending upon their schedule. The entire family kept all hours. They were in this regard very much like their father.

"Billy up yet?" asked Joe, taking his seat at the kitchen table.

"It's Friday. He's off," reminded Mrs. Ball, removing her finger, and dropping her head back into the paper.

Billy was the oldest of three very big, very scrappy, similarly bullet-headed boys, none of whom possessed an ounce of athletic ability. But they did love to fight. Billy was the biggest and the most lethal brother. Once in a fight, Billy gained a kind of mutant strength that intensified until he crushed his adversary. He also possessed an uncanny ability to identify an opponent's weakness, a useful trait in the bars where he bounced. Just a week ago, he ended a fight by sticking his fingers into the oversized nostrils of a misbehaving patron and hurled him out into the street by his nose. All of this was common knowledge inside the Ball household and most of the North End. As a result, Billy was a frequent victim of the un-telegraphed sucker punch, his only known weakness.

The Ball brothers spent much of their time stress-testing each other. But they all agreed on one thing: they were catching up to their father. In their youth, patrolman Ball was a street legend full of swag and stories, capable of taking them all, which he did regularly. Now, the boys got their own swag and the old man's stories were starting to run together. He was still a presence, just not an icon.

The middle son was eating cereal, while his younger brother fried up a burger with onions. Billy entered the kitchen, sized up the situation, and opted for the cereal. Four melon-headed bodies bobbed around the kitchen, retrieving plates, spoons, milk, salt, pepper, ketchup, sugar, coffee and soda, eggs or meat, depending on whether they were eating breakfast, lunch or dinner.

"Ran into Butch Mahon this morning," said Joe.

The two brothers looked up from reading the back of their cereal boxes. Mrs. Ball placed her finger on the newspaper. A plane landing at Newark Airport roared overhead. It seemed inches away from the roof and shook the house down to its studs. This happened whenever the wind shifted out of the north and the planes needed to fly over Elizabeth to land safely. Like all Northenders, Joe reflexively raised his voice a few decibels to be heard.

"CAUGHT HIM IN A HOT CADDY. RIGHT ON BROAD STREET," shouted Joe.

"YOU LET HIM GO?" yelled Billy.

"YEAH."

This was hardly news. The boys returned to their cereal boxes and Mrs. Ball removed her finger from the newspaper. The plane landed. Joe lowered his voice and tried again.

"So, Billy, what are you doing today?"

"Meeting the boys tonight at the K Tavern. Going into the city with Jackie now."

"What for?"

"Don't know yet. We'll find something."

This was true. Billy Ball and Jackie Martin had been close friends since their school days together at St. Catherine's. Whenever they got together, things just happened, often the most improbable things. Like the time as kids they walked every floor of the all-Black, always dangerous, Dayton Street projects to retrieve their stolen bicycles and miraculously emerged unscathed. Or the time they managed to get a moving violation inside of a car wash. Or the time they ran into each other on a long-range patrol in the jungles of Vietnam. Jackie Martin was the de facto fourth brother in the Ball home, and Billy extended to him the same bouncer-like protections he gave to the rest of the family. They would undoubtedly find something to do in New York City. The thought of tacking on a few beers with the boys at the K Tavern made the next twelve hours even more appealing.

The familiar car horn of Jackie's Pinto beeped in the driveway. Billy got up from the table to go. He walked past his younger brother at the stove and took a rabbit punch to the back of the head, which knocked him forward a step. Billy dipped his shoulder, plowed into his brother, and pinned him against the counter. From this position of moral superiority,

Billy pounded the back of his brother's head with a flurry of roundhouses. The hamburger, the onions and several dishes crashed to the floor.

"Out of my kitchen," said Mrs. Ball above the din. "Joe, get my spoon."

The spoon. Mrs. Ball wielded the long wooden spoon as both weapon and gavel. She took it and whacked them both until the boys ceased hostilities and they all began to laugh. When it was over, the three of them stood panting and grinning at each other, amused at their absurd, predictable selves

"I'm going to turn in," said Joe, stretching his arms over his head.

CHAPTER 2

Peterstown

"Shut your mouth when you're talking to me."
– Anthony Fabrizio

The Peterstown card game broke up around 9:00 am. Two hours earlier, Jimmy Grillo had broken everybody's back by drawing an inside straight against a full pot. Never a gracious winner, Jimmy stuck around and tormented the losers by re-living his winning hand – over and over and over. The losers grunted and dragged themselves up the basement stairs onto Elizabeth Avenue. The bright morning sun, most unwelcome after 16 straight hours of poker, further afflicted the losers. But the day looked good to Jimmy Grillo, who had a rare good night at the table. With a wad of other people's money in his pocket and a song in his heart, Jimmy thought it shameful to waste such a good mood on mere sleep. He turned up Elizabeth Avenue in search of coffee, eggs, and toast to prolong the moment.

Jimmy's walk in the sun was cut short. His bookie, Anthony Fabrizio, chose this moment to take an early morning constitutional on the streets.

"Just thinking about you, Jimmy," said Anthony. "And here you are."

Jimmy owed Anthony six grand, about half the size of his winnings, minus breakfast.

"Let's take a walk," said Anthony. "By the river."

Anthony, short and gelatinous, aspired to great things within the DeCavalcante crime family. His desire to please outstripped his brains. But he did have good contacts on the street. When Anthony heard about Jimmy's unlikely run at the table, he roused himself and headed over to the game – just in time to catch Jimmy before his many other creditors.

Jimmy owed everybody in Peterstown – the landlord, the bar, the grocer, former friends – and most urgently, Anthony. Jimmy eked out a living running numbers for the DeCavalcantes. But that racket dried up when a new gang came to town and muscled him out. The new gang ran out of Trenton. They were ruthless, powerful, and well-protected by the state. In fact, they *were* the state. In 1975, the state of New Jersey introduced the Pick 3, an innovation that replaced the local *numbers* con with a state-wide *lottery* con. Pointy-headed officials sitting in the state capital followed up with the Pic 4. Pretty soon, Jimmy was out of a job. In a singularly ill-timed move, he started running a roulette table for the DeCavalcantes – a year before the state legalized gambling in Atlantic City. Still more hard luck. Still more bureaucrat-mobsters eating his lunch. The success of the Trenton gang left Jimmy demoralized and without a clear career path. The DeCavalcantes lacked a job re-training program, so Jimmy fell back on his own scant resources. These consisted of sports betting and card-playing for his own account, where his unrelenting run of bad luck continued.

John (the Eagle) Riggi had taken over the big Elizabeth crime family after Sam (the Plumber) DeCavalcante went to prison. The Plumber actually owned a plumbing fixture business, but his real passion ran beyond T pipes to gambling and pornography stores. Behind 2,300 transcript pages of FBI tapes (known as the Goodfella tapes in another case of mob life imitating art), he pled guilty to a $20 million gambling ring and got seven years.

The Eagle cut a more courtly figure than the Plumber. Always well-dressed in suits and cuff links, Riggi made his white collar living as the business agent for the Laborers International Union of North America Local 394 of Elizabeth. As business agent, Riggi demanded and received kickbacks from construction firms in exchange for lower union wages and more relaxed safety rules on job sites. His oversight of the welfare and pension plans provided additional opportunities to serve the union movement. He skimmed worker benefits into his own pocket by providing an imaginative suite of professional services to the pension fund – everything from accounting to travel to escorts. The grateful brothers of Local 394 also paid Riggi a handsome salary for his trouble. And if anyone complained? Well, they just didn't.

Fleecing the union was a full-time job, and it could be

quite stressful for Riggi. So many opportunities to serve, so little time. In search of a better work-life balance, The Eagle relaxed with more traditional pastimes like loan sharking, extortion, hijacking and other gambling rackets as yet undiscovered by the Trenton gang.

In 1978, La Cosa Nostra had reached the height of its power in the New York metropolitan area. They owned the vice trade — old reliables like gambling and prostitution — and growing new ones like drugs. They had more money on the street than most banks. Few local businesses could avoid their exortionate "bite." They dominated the unions, and through them, basic industries like construction and transportation. They ran the fish market at South Street Seaport in Manhattan. They ran the meat and produce markets at Hunt's Point in the Bronx. In the New York metropolitan region, the mob controlled food, shelter and transportation – three of the four essentials of life. They had not yet figured out a way to monetize the air.

The remarkable success of La Cosa Nostra in the *new* world rested on a feudal code brought over from the *old* world. The lords of the manor – the bosses of the crime families – demanded oaths of loyalty and service. The serfs – the capos and soldiers – gave them willingly. This medieval system of intensely *personal* obligation thrived in the intensely *impersonal* city of New York. Against all odds, simple vows of allegiance defeated the combined forces of congressional hearings, public outcry and cutting-edge police work.

The feudal code required the serfs to earn money and pay tribute to their lord. In exchange, the lord protected the serfs from other lords who might have designs on their business. The code was unwritten, but universally understood. Unspoken, but quite clearly heard. Nowhere but everywhere. A favor bank for mobsters.

Jimmy had fallen outside the protection of his lord, John Riggi. He did not earn. He did not pay. With his mounting gambling debts, he actually *owed* money up the chain. The Eagle considered this an affront to the natural order of things. He might give Jimmy another chance. Riggi had many serfs under his protection – some enterprising, some lazy, some smart, some dumb. But there was no place for an unlucky gambler. The Eagle decided it was time to downsize his organization by a head – Jimmy's. The only question was when. Ideally, Riggi would like to collect the money Jimmy owed before killing him. Unbeknownst to Jimmy, his great run at the table was also a death sentence.

Anthony and Jimmy walked down Centre Street past the little retail stores that scratched out a living from the jumble of two-family houses on the street. They had grown up together in Peterstown, a few years apart but with a shared taste for the rackets. They walked past St. Anthony's, where both attended grammar school (and later high school together at Roselle Catholic) where Jimmy had tormented the little fat kid who grew into the big fat kid now holding the whip hand over him. They entered the narrow park (really more of a flood bank held together with weeds), which was empty most days – and always at this time of the morning. Jimmy expected to lose most of his winnings to Anthony. He did not expect to be murdered. He was surprised when Anthony pulled out a gun and pointed it at him. Anthony had never killed before. He had been coached to make it quick – no hesitation, no eye contact, above all no explanations. But as Anthony stood with his gun in Jimmy's face, he felt a strange rush run through his mozzarella-clogged veins. He enjoyed the look of abject terror on Jimmy's face. The look said 'I will do anything you want. You, Anthony Fabrezio, are a boss.' Unwilling to end such a delicious moment, Anthony held the gun steady. Maybe he could get Jimmy to beg a little.

Why, Jimmy wondered, am I still alive? Was this just a scare tactic? His mind cleared. Then he saw his chance, his only chance.

"Don't you want my money?" said Jimmy.

"Shut your mouth when you're talking to me. Besides, I'll get it after."

"That might leave fingerprints," said Jimmy helpfully.

"Oh, yeah. Hand it to me."

"Okay."

Jimmy found his wad and cautiously extended it. Anthony leveled his eyes on Jimmy. Then, Jimmy deliberately dropped the money to ground. For a moment, Anthony's greed overcame his gun-inflated ego. He dropped awkwardly down on one knee to retrieve the money. He took his eyes off Jimmy for a second. Jimmy bolted. Anthony closed his eyes and fired five shots after him. All missed. Almost out of pistol range, Jimmy's bad streak caught up to him for the last time. The sixth bullet found the back of Jimmy's luckless head. His face went away. The force of the last shot pushed him forward. Jimmy took a few more dead man steps. Then he dropped to the ground, falling conveniently behind a bush. The red pulp above his neck pumped blood into the dirt. Now Anthony was shocked. Not at the killing, which he enjoyed. But at the prospect that Jimmy had almost gotten away, and with it, his chances for advancement with the organization. Anthony was more eager to move up than a cub reporter at the *Daily Planet*.

"That was close," he reflected. "I should have just popped him like they said."

Anthony picked up the money. He placed the hot gun in the back of his belt, where it seared his back.

"What am I going to do with this gun?" he thought, forgetting that he had been told to drop the gun in the river.

A beat-up green Pinto stopped at the light on Fourth Avenue. Anthony recognized Jackie Martin in the driver's seat. They had played basketball against each other in the parochial grammar school league, where Jackie was a big star. He did not see Billy Ball sitting next to him. As the Pinto drove away, an idea, a really bad idea, slowly formed in Anthony's mind — an idea that would resolve the pressing matter of the murder weapon burning a brand onto his backside — an idea that would place Jackie Martin at the scene of the crime.

CHAPTER 3

Singers

"Begorra." – Mario Calabrese

Patrick dumped the eggshells and coffee grounds into the dirt. He mixed them in with a rake to form the secret compost that made the tomatoes grow so well. It was only July and the plants already stood five feet tall and heavy with fruit, proof again that the old family recipe for fertilizer brought over from Calabria still worked in the new world. Already 95 degrees at 10:00 am in the morning, Patrick was glad to have the weeding done for the day.

Patrick's father, Mario Calabrese, prepared another more pungent, and even more secret, compost for the grapes at the other end of the garden near the house. He tended his vines with an experienced and loving hand, looking more like a *paisan* on a Calabrian hillside than an underemployed millhand in the concretized swamps of Elizabeth, New Jersey.

Together, Mario and Patrick cultivated every inch of the tiny garden behind their miniature white stone house in Peterstown. The fertilized soil responded with enough tomatoes and eggplant to see the family through October of each year. A wooden trellis ran the length of the yard. It produced ten boxes of grapes a year, which Patrick and his father fermented in their dirt floor basement.

Mario Calabrese made his living as an unskilled laborer at the Singer factory, an enormous affair. Mario staged rough plates of steel early in the manufacturing process, plates that would ultimately become the treadles of the world-famous Singer sewing machine. So large was the factory that he rarely saw the finished machines that emerged from the other end of the production line, a half-mile away. Mario's hours, along with those of the dwindling workforce, had recently been cut. Under the new regime, Mario stayed home on Fridays.

The Singer factory works sat on the Jersey side of the Arthur Kill, which provided tidewater passage to New York Harbor. The factory covered 113 acres and, at its peak, employed 10,000 people. Attracted by easy water access, cheap land, and a clever industrial workforce good with their hands, Isaac Singer built the Elizabeth works in 1863. Undeterred by that pesky Civil War going on in the faraway land of Dixie, Singer set up his five-story red brick factory to consolidate four different production facilities into one vertically integrated behemoth of efficiency. Here, in the largest factory ever built in the U.S., the citizens of Elizabeth met to produce, stage, and ship sewing machines all over the world.

Before Isaac Singer invented his sewing machine, women

toiled at home with a single needle and thread to clothe their large families. The hyper-efficient sewing machine produced ten times more clothing in the same amount of time and gave a sudden jolt of productivity to the female half of earth. Freed from the drudgery of hand sewing, women took their first faltering steps into the workforce outside the home.

There were consequences.

With women producing more and more clothing with less and less effort, prices fell. Then, the wages of seamstresses fell. In *Das Kapital*, Karl Marx foretold that falling wages caused by the Singer sewing machine would create a worker revolt. Capitalism would inevitably eat itself following the immutable laws of history that only he could see. Conservatives decried the erosion of the traditional family. Politicians everywhere took their piece of the action with tariffs. Much talk about justice, freedom, and values. One thing was crystal clear: the women of the world had united. They wanted more sewing machines and they were going to get them.

The manufacture of sewing machines required enormous fixed costs in the form of real estate, machinery, and equipment. To offset this mountain of overhead, the business needed an even bigger mountain of sales. Isaac Singer needed more volume, always more volume, to run through his gigantic factories and make them pay. If he ran enough volume to cover his overhead, each new sale fell into his bank account as profit, like penny candy into the pocket of a child.

Singer found volume in the far-distant corners of the world where others had not thought to look. He realized that the same machine could be used by women from many different cultures to relieve the universal misery of hand sewing. And so, volume grew. His partner, a buttoned-up WASPy lawyer with an unexpected gift for salesmanship, pioneered the layaway plan. And volume grew again. Singer built factories in foreign lands and captured entire countries. Volume exploded.

The grinding law of big numbers made Singer and his partners the wealthiest men on earth. Together, they took a uniquely American private gamble that the biggest, most intimidating investment would yield the biggest, most intimidating profits on a global scale. They won that gamble and created the first U.S. multi-national corporation. Dipping into spare cash, they built the tallest building in the world in New York City to serve as their corporate offices. The Singer name became the first global brand, outside of the Bible and the Koran.

After World War II, the fortunes of Singers began to wane. American homemakers preferred to buy new, cheap ready-to-wear clothes rather than mend the old ones, no matter how efficiently it might be done. Singers was indeed being taken down by the masses — just not the proletarian ones. The death blow came from mass consumers, affluent housewives who ushered in the next wave of feminism by buying off the rack.

The federal government, eager to entice their former foes away from siren song of Communism, shared the fruits of freedom by opening the U.S. market to cheap foreign imports. In exchange, the world got to see just how good life could be within the American orbit. The federales dropped tariffs on imported sewing machines and turned a blind eye to foreign subsidies. By 1953, born-again Japanese democrats exported 1.3 million machines, nine times more than their best year before the war, mostly to the United States.

Now the law of big numbers, so long the engine of profits, began to work against the company. Decreasing sales volume exposed the bloated overhead of the business, which had grown unchecked during the fat years. Profits fell. Hands were wrung. New leadership decided that the problems of the sewing machine business, which they understood all too well, could be fixed by buying up businesses they knew nothing about. Accepting the received wisdom of the age, management set about turning Singers into a conglomerate. They spun off the sewing machine business and closed their biggest factories in Elizabeth and Scotland. They borrowed heavily to acquire assets in electronics and aerospace, the hot technologies of their day. In the spirit of the times, the new men claimed that bundling unrelated businesses under one corporate roof somehow reduced the risk of all of them.

This worked for a while. Then the stock market crashed in 1987. Sensing that Singers' stock price was lower than the sum of its parts, a new set of financial engineers moved in. Led by Paul Bilzerian and financed by T. Boone Pickens, these corporate raiders took over the conglomerate formerly known as Singers. Within four weeks, Bilzerian sold seven of twelve business and made $256 million.

There followed a number of wannabe raiders who tried hard to catch the Bilzerian golden ring by hitching one last ride on the broken-down merry-go-round that Singers had become. The new raiders showed more interest in boardroom hijinks than in solving the problems of their customers. Even Marx could have predicted the outcome. The final years of Singers provided a sad punctuation to the old saying: every business starts out as a movement and ends up as a racket. The last financial engineer to step on the merry-go-round was Kolberg, the first K in KKR. Kolberg bought the original sewing machine business. He moved production to emerging countries where impoverished women still sought to gain their first toehold on the economic ladder. There, in the forgotten unelectrified lands of the poor, the durable little sewing machine, powered by foot pedals, re-captured its former glory. Long dead in the first world, Isaac Singer's magic contraption still worked its wonders in the third. There, the Singer name lived on, an indestructible value that no financial bone picker could diminish.

Thus came the hours of Mario Calabrese to be reduced at the Singers Sewing Machine Works.

Patrick's mother stuck her head out of the kitchen window.

"Come into your breakfast now before it gets cold, and I have to throw it out," she said in her Irish accent, still as thick as when she landed in New York thirty years ago.

Patrick was an anomaly. His father immigrated from Calabria as a young boy and grew up in Peterstown, the Italian section of Elizabeth. Actually, Mario grew up in a Calabrian village re-created within Peterstown. This imaginary village was tight, closed to anyone from Sicily or Naples, let alone the other mongrel hordes of Elizabeth, who were

deeply distrusted by the Italian tribes, who in turn deeply
distrusted each other. But within the Calabrian village, everyone passed for "uncle" or "aunt" or "cousin" in the Italian
way, regardless of blood lines.

So it was with some concern that the Calabrian clans of
Elizabeth met and sized up the elfin Bridget, Patrick's mother
from County Cork, Ireland. Bridget had a few relatives in New
York but found herself otherwise alone in the broad United
States. With no knowledge of the Italian language and even
less of its cuisine, Bridget nevertheless nurtured her inner
Calabrese with great joy. Like the way she lovingly boiled the
raviolis to their lumpy death. Or her remedy of substituting
ketchup for tomato sauce in a pinch. She eventually won the
village over with her love of all things Calabrian, however
imperfectly embraced. Patrick (the only one in Peterstown)
was a striking young man with red hair, freckles and dark
eyes, an only child, which made him more exceptional still.
His full name, Patrick Calabrese, told the tale of his mixed-up
blood and attracted a good deal of derision from the Sicilians
every time they heard it.

Patrick took off his work gloves and returned the rake
to the narrow tool shed at the back of the yard. Mario walked
up the three back steps into the kitchen. Mario didn't wear
any gloves because his calloused hands *were* gloves.

"Hey, Patrick," came a whisper from the other side of
the trellis. "It's me, Anthony."

"What?" said Patrick.

"You gotta do something for me."

Anthony Fabrizio was one of the Sicilian street urchins

who had made Patrick's life miserable as a child. In the argot of Peterstown, a most unpromising start to a conversation.

"Like what?"

"Hide this for me."

Anthony passed him a gun through the trellis, the barrel pointed toward Patrick.

"No way."

"Come on."

"No."

"You would be doing your buddy Jackie a big favor."

"How's that?"

"He just used it."

Patrick touched the barrel. It was still warm.

"Take it. I gotta go – now."

Anthony released the butt of the gun, and it fell into Patrick's hand. Anthony's stubby fingers disappeared behind the vines. He was gone. Patrick placed the gun behind the tool shed and went inside. Mario sat at the table sipping his black expresso out of a tiny cup made for the purpose, Bridget her mug of tea with milk. They were waiting for him to start in.

"You right, Patrick?" asked Bridget, noting his eyes that were still dazed from his exchange with Anthony. His red freckles lit up against his pale face.

"Right as rain," he said, speaking in the Irish expressions he sometimes used to make himself understood to her. She looked hard at her only child, unconvinced, and pulled up a chair close to him.

"Que pasta?" she said, mixing up her scant Italian with her minimal Spanish and tussling his hair.

Patrick dug into his spaghetti, bacon, and eggs. He felt better as his mother's interpretation of breakfast slid down his throat. The coloring slowly returned to his face.

Patrick's breath slowed, but his mind was alert, shooting down possible explanations as fast as they popped up, like the bad guys in a shooting gallery. Jackie Martin mixed up with Anthony? Very unlikely. Pop! With the DeCavalcante's? Never. Pop-pop! Jackie firing off a gun in Peterstown at ten in the morning? Impossible. Pop-pop-pop! Was Anthony lying? Possible, quite possible. Why had Anthony come to him?

Growing up in Peterstown, Patrick had been surrounded by wise guys all his life. He was never tempted by the racketeers, clearly a Sicilian thing of theirs, and theirs alone. Perhaps more importantly, *they* had no interest in *him*, an untrustworthy half-breed with alien red hair and freckles. All the more troubling that Anthony would come to him now in his time of need. Why? He barely knew Anthony. And how did Anthony know Jackie?

Half-way through his breakfast, another frightening bad guy popped up in his imagination. What if the gun *had* really been used in a crime, maybe a murder? What if this was a set-up? What if Anthony was telling the cops right now that the gun was in his yard, warm and with his fingerprints? His fingerprints! Maybe he should wipe the gun clean like in the movies?

"Watched *Casablanca* last night on the late show," said Bridget.

Patrick looked up and wondered for the millionth time just how many of his thoughts his mother could read.

"It's a great one," he said.

"Bogey and Bergman," she sighed.

They sat quietly while each replayed their favorite scenes from the movie. They were the same scenes, as they both well knew from previous discussions.

"All I know is that the problems of three people," said Patrick, starting his favorite line.

"Don't amount to a hill of beans in this crazy world," said Bridget dreamily.

"Someday you'll understand that," finished Patrick.

They quoted lines back and forth over breakfast. *Casablanca* changed Patrick's life. Before *Casablanca*, he was an easy-going kid who thought he would work on the assembly line at Singers with his father. After *Casablanca*, he saw the factory floor as a series of shots to be edited. Before, he was content to live out his life on the streets of the imaginary Calabrian village. After, he really wanted to direct a movie about the place. Before, Bridget's taste in movies ran to *Going My Way* and *The Bells of St. Mary's* and re-runs of cop shows. After, she dabbled with the *avant garde* and had lots of opinions on directors like Herzog and Fassbinder.

Patrick spent every waking hour watching movies and studying cinema at Rutgers at night. He dreamt in technicolor. As a young man whose ambitions exceeded his scratch, he financed this lifestyle as a part-time copy boy at the *Daily Journal*.

Bridget got up to clear the table. "I heard there may be more layoffs at Singers," she said.

"Begorra," said Mario, his tiny cup of espresso hovering

in the air.

Patrick didn't want to think about the possibility that his father's hours might be cut further. He turned his mind back to the gun sitting behind the tool shed. Too risky to leave it there, especially with Anthony in the wind.

"I'm going out," he said to his mother. Do you need anything?"

"Just cigarettes," said Bridget.

Without a fully formed plan of what to do next,

Patrick walked out the back door to the shed. Using the back door to get to the street drew no suspicion from his parents. In Peterstown, everybody kept a "good room" at the front of the house – white, plastic-covered furniture, white shag carpet and gilded lamps. The "good room" was never used – no matter how tiny the house. In the event of a fire, the family would rather flee through the windows than leave footprints on the shag rug of the "good room". Patrick looked over his shoulder for potential witnesses. He slipped the gun into his waistband, Bogey-like. More fingerprints, he thought. Patrick walked toward the candy store on Elizabeth Avenue, feeling the still-warm barrel of the gun pressing against his skin.

Just then, a green Pinto pulled up, and Billy rolled down the passenger window.

"We were looking for you. We're going into New York. You in?"

"Sure," said Patrick. He felt again for the gun and got into Jackie's Pinto.

CHAPTER 4

The Bayway Refinery

"Get yourself a new suit – anything but brown."
– Price Waterhouse audit partner

Stan Trykta looked down the long horseshoe bar of the Blue Moon tavern and took inventory. An experienced bartender, he knew the state of every drink and every drinker in the place. He knew who needed a refill, who could wait and who could not. The patrons were all men, all workers a few hours off the night shift from the nearby Bayway Refinery, just about all Polish. It was almost 11:00 in the morning – dinner time. Most would still be here eight hours later.

At 23, Stan stood tall and broad, quite fit from a lifetime of hard-nosed pickup basketball. A boyish lock of brown hair curled down over the center of his forehead. Stan wore glasses, the only one in the bar. He was generally disliked for it. In the view of the men at the bar, Stan was not a regular guy, not someone who would end up working in the refinery, day-drinking in the Blue Moon on a Friday morning. He had been away to college. He came back with ideas that went well beyond the red plastic stools that ringed the bar. They sensed in Stan certain alien aspirations that transcended the routine of baptisms, holy communions and funerals that capped the milestones of life in this traditional Polish neighborhood. To the men of the Blue Moon, Stan looked like someone who might someday slide off a red plastic stool, walk out the door and never return, someone who silently disapproved of them for reasons they only dimly understood. Someone with – glasses.

The Bayway Refinery sat on the Arthur Kill, a narrow waterway that opened up into New York Harbor to the north and Raritan Bay to the south. In the age of sail, westbound passengers from New York ferried to this spot in Elizabeth and then crossed the narrow waist of New Jersey in horse-drawn coaches. Poor roads made the overland trip into a bumpy, spine-jarring affair: muddy in spring, dusty in summer, freezing in winter. Quite expensive all the time. From there, the downstream currents of the Delaware River swept them to Philadelphia, the Chesapeake Bay and points further south. The strong flow of water into the Delaware Bay made it impossible to return upstream against the current. Instead, travelers tacked their way home to New York via ocean-going vessels that hugged the coast – when wind and wave permitted.

Moving freight was a bit easier. Horses dragged barges across upstate tributaries to the Hudson River. The produce was transferred to flatboats and floated down river to New York City, where it was off-loaded. Rather than attempt the trip back upstream, the flatboats were broken up for lumber. River currents pre-determined the movements of men and constrained their imaginations. Animals provided the muscle. Pretty much unchanged from the time of the ancients.

And then, in 1807, Robert Fulton mounted a steam engine on a boat. For the first time in human history, people and freight could travel upstream! Rivers became two-way highways. The same riverboat could be used twice! In time, capricious winds and currents gave way to schedules and timetables, designed by men for the convenience of men. Steamboats paddled up the Hudson River to deliver high-end European imports all the way to the Ohio Valley, opening up vast new markets. The steamboats also delivered another European import: people, who populated the newly accessible interior. Back in Elizabeth, shipyards sprang up on the Arthur Kill to meet the exploding demand.

And then, in 1830, George Stephenson, inventor of the steam locomotive, opened the first railway. Soon, two-way river traffic itself seemed ancient. Why restrict yourself to rivers when rails could take you anywhere you wanted to go? Which turned out to be everywhere. Railroads spread out over the continent like antennae sensing and searching for new markets. Railroads required coal for fuel. Coal required railroads for transport. Both needed farms and towns along the way. The two new industries grew together exponentially, each one pushing the other to new heights. As an afterthought, the population of the United States tripled.

And then the pace really picked up.

In 1844, Samuel Morse strung together the first working telegraph and eliminated distance altogether. The idea caught on. In twelve years, a transatlantic cable connected the new world to the old.

In 1854, Dr. Abraham Gesner put oil under pressure and created kerosene, a cheap illuminant that replaced candles and, much to the relief of whales, whale oil. The only drawback was the creation of unwanted by-products like gasoline and asphalt, which had no practical use.

In 1875, Alexander Bell invented the telephone, which replaced the telegraph.

In 1885, Karl Benz invented the first gas-powered automobile, which replaced the already antiquated steam engine. And, in the process, solved the problem of what to do with all that useless gasoline and asphalt.

Which was a good thing for the oil business because Thomas Edison had already replaced kerosene with electricity when he lit up Lower Manhattan in 1882.

In 1903, the Wright brothers found another use for gasoline when Orville flew across the sands of Kitty Hawk in the first airplane.

And then, after one hundred years of dizzying, world-shrinking advances, progress in transportation came to an end. As abruptly as it started back in 1807, innovation stopped. Nothing replaced the telephone, electricity, or the light bulb. Nothing replaced the internal combustion engines used to power trains, cars, and airplanes. Nothing replaced the need for gasoline, oil, and asphalt.

In 1907, John Rockefeller, with his sharp eye for the sure thing, built the Bayway Refinery on the Arthur Kill in Elizabeth. Like all things Rockefeller, it was a colossal undertaking, ultimately covering 1,600 acres. With easy access to New York harbor, the refinery supplied the entire New York metropolitan area with gasoline. As was his way, Rockefeller lowered his prices and drove the other local refineries out of business. In the absence of competitors, the Bayway Refinery captured the New York market. Just like the telephone, electricity, the light bulb and the internal combustion engine, nothing could replace the gasoline produced by the Bayway Refinery.

And nothing could *change* the Bayway Refinery. The original cracking process developed by Dr. Gesner proved to be remarkably durable. The crackers grew larger, yields improved, octane increased, but the basic process of turning oil into gasoline remained essentially unchanged. And dangerous.

Crude oil is both flammable and volatile. When mixed with catalysts and subjected to extreme heat, it becomes even more so. Under high pressure, a cracker can turn oil into a herd of wild horses, stampeding in any direction except the one laid down by the engineers. Explosions happen. Workers get vaporized. At the Bayway Refinery, the latest in a long line of mishaps occurred in 1970, when an explosion threw up flames 1,000 feet high and shook homes forty miles away.

A large Polish community lived and worked in the shadow of the Bayway Refinery. Rockefeller petro-bucks circulated through this company town and supported thousands of families. The families, in turn, supported Polish delicatessens, Polish bars like the Blue Moon, the beloved parish of St. Hedwig's and ultimately, Polish funeral homes. The Bayway Refinery gave life to St. Hedwig's, but it also extracted a price. If living next to a ticking time bomb was not enough, the Russians had sited the Bayway Refinery as a primary target for their nuclear missiles. New York City was a secondary target, which did little to re-assure the parishioners of St. Hedwig's, who lived in-between the two. Even in the new world, the Poles of St. Hedwig's could not escape the reach of the Russian bear.

For 70 years, sons followed fathers into the Bayway Refinery. And then grandsons. Union work rules were handed down at the dinner table from generation to generation pretty much unchanged, like the refinery itself. The seniority system effectively mapped out the remainder of their lives with incremental pay increases and promotions based on time spent in the refinery. Always time spent in the refinery. Until there was no more time. Working in a closed union shop and living next to a blast site between two nuclear targets imbued St. Hedwig's with a kind of quiet desperation that was, likewise, passed down from generation to generation. As much as the families of St. Hedwig's disliked living in a perpetual state of low-grade anxiety, they disliked the idea of changing it even more. Instead, they grew accustomed to the anxiety, like a troublesome mother-in-law living on the third floor.

Thus came the men of the Blue Moon to sit on their red plastic stools, day drinking on a Friday morning.

Stan's family owned the Blue Moon. His ancestors built and filled St. Hedwig's Church. They attended the adjacent parish grammar school. His large extended family worked on the waterfront, in the refinery and in a clutter of little retail businesses. Very few of them ever left St. Hedwig's, and so they multiplied.

Stan's family was, of course, political. There were simply too many of them not to be heard and their concerns were noted all the way up to the courthouse on Broad Street. Their main concern was simple: nothing was ever going to change at St. Hedwig's. The Irish might leave Elizabeth (the founding Anglos were long gone, vanished into the great American social experiment). Fleeing Cubans might replace the fleeing Irish. But the Polish parishioners of St. Hedwig's would have it understood that they intended to stay on forever, a fact that politicians would ignore at their peril. As a testament to the enduring political clout of St. Hedwig's, the mayor of Elizabeth, Tommy Dunn himself, sat at the bend of the horseshoe bar nursing a beer.

Tommy Dunn was a fireplug of a man: stubby with short arms — spraying out orders, jokes and demands in all directions. The patrons of the Blue Moon had been quietly watching Dunn since he arrived. They knew him, of course, by reputation and by his naturally gregarious nature. But today he had a quiet aura about him, a force field that said he was here on business. They did not engage.

Stan's mother Florence emerged from the kitchen carrying two plates of kielbasa. The smell of garlic and fresh thyme trailed behind her. She was a short, high-energy woman with bouffant hair that stood up high on her diminutive head as if it were electrified. All day long Florence walked in and out of the beauty shops, butchers, florists, funeral homes, bakeries, and bars of St. Hedwig's, each one owned by a member of her extended family. She kept them all humming with a complex mix of loans, favors, marriages and, to put it mildly — oversight. She assisted her family where she could and hammered them where she could not. In her already long life, no one had ever seen her drive a car, let alone leave the parish. Always just too much to do. She reigned alone as the matriarch of the Tryktas, not by election or popularity, but because it would be too exhausting to oppose her. Short a waitress, she was helping Stan this morning at the Blue Moon. She set down the plates in front of a couple of workers and walked over to Tommy Dunn.

"Something to eat?" she asked, pulling a pencil magically out of her high hair, as if Dunn were a roustabout at the refinery.

"No thanks, got a thing later," said Dunn politely, who knew perfectly well when *he* was in the presence of political royalty. "How have you been?"

"Got a funeral tomorrow."

"I heard. I will be there."

"Shame."

"Comes to us all."

After a moment of respectful silence, Dunn got down to business, knowing that his audience with Florence would be brief. She was already scanning the patrons around the bar and might light off at any moment to re-fill a drink or take a food order.

"I can't run your nephew for council," he said.

At this, Florence stopped her waitressing and looked hard

at the mayor. She didn't need to know the reason for the slight, but she did need to know what he would offer in return.

"Five jobs in sanitation. Two teachers and a building inspector. Gotta big federal contract coming."

She did the political math in her head quickly, as though adding up a big check, which in a way it was: who to appease at St. Hedwig's with a loan or a spouse, who to reward with the new jobs, how this news would ripple through the parish. Above all, how it might change the larger political dynamic of Elizabeth.

Florence enjoyed a good deal of influence in the city. By sheer numbers, the Poles of St. Hedwig's dominated the electoral politics of the 2nd ward. The Tryktas dominated the parish through their control of senior union positions at the refinery. Florence dominated the Trykta clan by her life-force.

Florence Trykta knew everyone in the 2nd who needed a job, a favor, maybe some cash to get through a dry patch. Who needed to be fired, denied, cast out. More importantly, she knew the difference between the two. Punish a loyal soldier and you made an enemy for life. Reward a traitor and you woke up with a knife in your back. And she knew the families. How a favor or a slight might ripple through the voting patterns of many households. The key was to know the people she could trust to vote the line and those she could not. Always vote the line. And within the city limits of Elizabeth, there was no better judge of political horseflesh than Florence Trykta. Although Florence did not hold any elected position, she was a vital cog in the political machine of Tom Dunn.

To the casual observer, the political operation of Tom Dunn looked like any other big city machine: favors for votes, jobs for votes, cash for votes. But in reality, the Dunn machine operated on loyalty, often generational loyalty, that ran both ways between the mayor and the voters. As proof of his longevity, Tom Dunn currently occupied the mayor's chair for the fourth of ultimately seven consecutive terms, the most of any big city mayor in the country.

The machine operated along the same lines as the favor bank of the cops and the feudal code of the mob. Each system hung on an unwritten (and unforgiving) set of obligations that bound all parties. The purpose of each system was the same: to preserve the organization and perpetuate the insiders who ran them. Without a clear understanding of the rules that governed the machine, the mob and the cops, Elizabeth appeared to be a chaotic place marred by random events where evil men prospered everywhere. Once the rules were understood, the city opened up. It became an easy matter to read the newspapers, to predict the behavior of one's fellow citizens, to get along.

Florence sized up the mayor's offer and decided it was more than fair, even generous: *three* jobs in sanitation and a construction contract being the standard exchange rate for the seat of a councilman.

"Okay, let me know."

"See you tomorrow."

Dunn slid off his red plastic stool. He pulled out a thick wad of walking-around money, and to the utter astonishment of the crowd, left an entire dollar bill on the bar as a tip. He paid the bill of the patron next to him and headed out the door, onto his next event. After Dunn left, the men of the Blue Moon sensed that something momentous had just taken place. They looked to Florence for an answer that remained locked behind her steel grey, grandmotherly eyes. It was not forthcoming. She scooped up the dollar and disappeared behind the swinging aluminum doors that led to the kitchen.

Florence did not include Stan in the political side of her affairs — the same way Don Corleone protected the young and talented Michael from the family business in *The Godfather*. He knew well enough not to ask about her brief but intense exchange with the mayor. Stan viewed the world as a disorderly place, one that would be much improved by a little organization and some tidying up, traits that made him singularly ill-suited to politics. To Stan, every action, however messy, needed to be weighed, balanced, and put neatly away. Stan was, in short, a born accountant, a destiny he embraced.

After many years of schooling, interrupted by varying stints in one retail storefront or another, Stan had finally gotten his degree. Stan, his mother, her clan, and the rest of St. Hedwig's assumed that he would be an accountant in the family business, probably the chief accountant. With Florence's backing, he would start his own local practice and create yet another arm of the Trykta empire. According to Florence's plan, Stan needed to run a financial reporting business to keep her informed about the health of all the others — a service that would at once serve and control them all. Stan was to be banker, accountant and financial advisor to the family, the financial hub around which all the little retail spokes would revolve. He would eventually assume all the commercial activities that now filled the busy bouffant of Florence Trykta. Thus liberated, Florence would move on to her true passion: Elizabeth politics.

As one of the few in the family to get a college degree, Stan felt the weight of great expectations. He was educated. He knew things no one else did. This knowledge would help guarantee the survival of the next generation, and, even more importantly, ensure that change bypassed St. Hedwig's. Until recently, Stan felt up to the challenge.

But now, Stan was not so sure. After he attended an on-campus recruiting session for Price Waterhouse, he began to have second thoughts. The recruiter discussed various career paths available to him in audit, tax, and consulting, not to mention the possibility of travel, perhaps even foreign travel. That life sounded exciting, glamorous. That life did not include keeping the books for a motley collection of storefront shops under the Goethals Bridge.

For his secret interview at the offices of Price Waterhouse, Stan had traveled to New York City, a mere ten miles away for a crow. But to the parishioners of St. Hedwig's, Manhattan was more remote than the Emerald City of Oz, a dazzling but forbidden place, one imagined more than visited. Stan himself had only been a few times, and never at rush hour. Fitted out in an old brown suit a size too small, Stan sat on the Staten Island ferry as it approached the skyline of Lower Manhattan, feeling like the lion, the tinman, the scarecrow and Dorothy all in one.

His anxiety grew as he filled out the application forms

in front of a large picture window with spectacular views of downtown New York — a window specifically designed to evoke such feelings in young interviewees like himself. He had never been so high in a building before. Planes buzzed too close to the window and unnerved him. Below on the streets, tiny people emerged from toy-like buses. They crawled over each other in a mad rush to get to their offices. Off in the distance the miniature Goethals Bridge pointed the way to a little mound that was the Isle of Staten. None of the busy people zooming around the office took any notice of the view, or him, or anything else for that matter. It looked to Stan as if the entire city was running late for a very important meeting about something he couldn't possibly understand. He waited two hours.

During his first interview, they talked about various careers he might pursue in high finance: mergers, acquisitions, spinoffs, initial public offerings. An hour and two interviews later, he embraced all of these career choices, and the brainy, urbane people who pitched them. His final interview was with a wizened old audit partner, who simply said:

"Get yourself a new suit — anything but brown."

That closed the deal for Stan. The partner, and indeed the entire firm, were committed to tidying up the world on a global scale. These were serious people who appealed to his serious nature with a calling, not just an occupation. He was determined to suit up (blue of course) and become one of them. Stan left the offices of Price Waterhouse like a man with courage, a heart, a brain, and a home. But what about his mother? She had already set him up with an office and long list of people to call. Meanwhile, Price Waterhouse was pressing him for a commitment. When to tell her? How to tell her? What to tell her?

Stan looked at the blue neon clock over the door of the Blue Moon and unconsciously removed twenty minutes in the conversion from bar time to Eastern Standard: 10:40. He was late. Florence emerged with two more plates of steaming kielbasa and set them down before a couple of patrons. As she headed back to the kitchen, Stan stopped her.

"I gotta go," he said.

"We're down a waitress."

"I know, I opened up this morning on my own."

"We're down a waitress."

"I made plans."

"What plans?"

"It's Jackie's birthday," he lied. "We're all meeting at the K Tavern later."

"It's only 11 o'clock. What? Are you getting him a present?"

Birthdays could (and would) be checked, but Florence already knew he was lying to her, and lying badly. Florence looked hard at her youngest child, the same hard look she had given the mayor when he told her about the council seat that had gone missing. Unlike the mayor, Stan did not have anything to offer his mother but an apology. She waited for it. A moment hung between them in the air like a high, lazy fly ball tumbling toward the fence, unclear if it was a home run or an easy out.

"I gotta go," he said at last, without the requisite apology.

Florence said nothing but turned and pushed aside the

battered doors to the kitchen. Stan's refusal to stay longer on the job did not amount to big deal, but his lying and lack of contrition certainly did. She sensed something had changed in her son, but the depth and meaning of that change were as yet unknown to her. He was growing up. Florence had seen rebellion before and had squashed it in her other five children, but this felt different. Stan was the good kid, the smart, diligent one who always showed up for work or anything else that needed doing. Stan was the future. The college boy. Florence weighed this concern in her quick mind and filed it away somewhere below the five new sanitation jobs to be filled, but above the flowers she needed for the funeral tomorrow. It would keep for now, unlike the next plate of kielbasa waiting to be served up.

Out on the street, Stan felt the artificial coolness of the Blue Moon leave the surface of his skin, replaced by a layer of hot moisture drifting in from the Arthur Kill. He needed to get downtown and buy a blue suit, a shirt and two ties. Stan walked to his car parked under the Goethals bridge. He paused and looked up at the thick cables that anchored the western terminus of the bridge into the soil of St. Hedwig's. In his harried mind, the woven steel ropes reminded him of the sinews of his family that bound him to this place: heavy, tight, unbreakable. He felt weighed down by the responsibility to his family and the need to defend an old-world lifestyle that was already passing. In his heart, he knew that someday it would all change and there was nothing he could do to stop it. He could see this quite clearly even if his mother could not. No, Stan yearned to be away from this hopeless struggle against the American melting pot, away from the fossilized sub-culture of the Bayway Refinery. He wanted the great adventure promised by Price Waterhouse, an adventure that would bring him wealth and sophistication, an adventure equal to his newly formed, more worldly, image of himself. But first he had to have a conversation with his mother. Today, when he refused to stay on at the bar, he had taken a small but significant step towards that conversation.

Stan crossed the street. Jackie, Billy, and Patrick rolled up in the green Pinto. Billy flagged him down.

"We're going into the city. You in?"

"Can't. Gotta go downtown."

"What for?"

"I need to buy a suit."

"That can't wait?"

"I have an interview on Monday."

"Okay. See you tonight at the K."

Stan got into his sensible blue Rambler and drove out of the mighty parish of St. Hedwig's in search of the perfect blue suit that would change everything.

CHAPTER 5

Downtown

"Description of the caller?" – Elizabeth P.D. Detective

"Walks with a limp" – Meg Murphy

"Which leg?"

"They just stole my purse," said the woman on the other end of the line.

"Where are you, Ma'am?" said Meg.

"Broad Street."

"Description?"

"White boys. Three white boys."

"Okay. Stay right where you are. I'll send a car over."

Meg disconnected the call and switched over to the radio.

"Car 24. We got a snatch and run on Broad. Three white boys."

"Victim?"

"Old lady."

"Description of the boys?"

"We just went over this."

"Okay, Meg. We're on our way."

Meg put down her radio headset and got up from her desk.

"I'm going for a Coke. Want anything?" she said to her fellow dispatcher.

"No, I'm good."

Meg Murphy stepped out of her shared, cramped office and into the hallway. Meg was half-Irish and half-Cuban, a fairly exotic mix for the time. With bronze skin and blonde hair, she wore a size 6 skirt that made the most of her trim figure. No makeup, no nails. She always wore her hair up to show off her long neck, which was more than enough. Her wide blue eyes gave the impression of innocence, even naivete. They deceived, as gullibility in no way formed any part of her character. Her clear instructions over the radio, no less than her wit and sharp tongue, were famous among the cops of the city. At twenty-three, she was already a legend in law enforcement circles. Her wisecracks circulated wherever cops gathered. None of them wanted to be caught on the wrong end of a *bon mot* from Meg on an open channel. They even had a name for it: to say something stupid and be called out for it was to be "megged," a play on "mugged," which accurately described the feelings of her victim. Her good looks, her slicing street smarts, and her willingness to weaponize both added to her mystique.

Meg took a pull off her Coke.

"What's this meeting about today?" she asked.

"Don't know. Something about a new dispatch system.

They call it 9-1-1."

"Does that stand for something?"

"Who knows."

Meg's line lit up and she answered the call.

"I just found a dead guy by the river," said the voice on the other end of the line. "In Peterstown."

"What's your name, sir?"

"Forget it."

"When did you discover the body?"

"A few minutes ago. I think he was shot."

"Did you hear anything?"

The line went dead. Meg put out a call to all cars in Peterstown.

"Got a dead soldier by the river. Not a drill, ladies!"

Word of the murder spread quickly from the dispatchers to the office workers to the cops to the detectives who were soon lined up at Meg's desk looking for more information. Three of them stood around her with open notepads scribbling down everything that she said.

"Description of the caller?" they asked for the fourth time.

"Walks with a limp," said Meg.

"Which leg?"

"Left."

One of the detectives stopped writing and looked up to see a small smile lift up the corners of Meg's delicate mouth. He smiled, too, and quietly watched his fellow detectives still bent over their pads.

"Anything else on the caller?"

"Big tattoo on his right arm."

The second detective looked up and smiled. They were all watching the third detective, the most aggressive, a Ukranian guy about thirty-five, still pouring notes into his pad.

"Anything else?"

Meg took another pull on her Coke, relaxed her arm, and let the can swing daintily from the tips of her long fingers. After one delicious moment, she swooped in for the kill.

"He was Ukranian."

The third detective stopped writing and looked up.

"Wait a minute. How can you tell that over the phone?"

He looked up from his pad at Meg and into her wide, traffic-light eyes. The other detectives laughed and folded up their notebooks. This one would be making the rounds tonight and the young detective knew it. Megged again.

"Joe Ball just found the body," said a dispatcher. "One in the head."

The detectives bolted from Meg's desk in hot pursuit of the next turn in the case. They were gone, out the door and onto the street, on their way to Peterstown in the urgent, self-important manner of all detectives. A young cop, a school-mate who grew up with Meg, walked up and sat on the edge of her desk.

"What do you think?" asked a long and lean Mike Burke. He had two pointed incisors, which gave every impression of a wolf.

Meg hunched up her shoulders, tilted her head, opened the palms of her hands, and lifted her eyes to the heavens in supplication, giving him the fullest expression of the Jersey shrug. If there was a subtitle under her, it would say 'What can I tell you?'

"Peterstown," she said.

"DeCavalcantes?"

"Most likely."

"The caller?"

"He's in on it."

Mike nodded and walked off. This was only sense. The murder of a civilian in Peterstown was less likely than Mayor Dunn letting someone else pick up his bar tab. The call was just a request to clean up the mess. And to notify the rest of the underworld that justice had been served out by the DeCavalcantes in Peterstown.

The thin blue line of the Elizabeth P.D. had grown much thinner of late as a crime wave engulfed the city. It showed no sign of abating. The rest of the state fared little better. Between 1960 and 1980, the New Jersey murder rate increased by 250 percent. Property crimes rose by 400 percent. Aggravated assault leapt by 430 percent. All violent crime rocketed up by 540 percent. In the destructive wake of the new violence, entire communities were reduced to rubble.

The new violence took many forms. There were old-fashioned crimes driven by greed and passion, relatively simple matters to understand and solve. Like killing your bookie to relieve a gambling debt. Or shooting your lover in the heat of the moment. All-too-human responses to all-too-human problems. This was old-school violence as practiced by the DeCavalcante's. Just business, really — human business. There was simply a lot more of it.

Then there were senseless crimes committed without

reason or remorse, without any discernable link between cause and effect, without any real advantage to the perpetrators. Like wasting a kid for his sneakers. Or shooting the owner of a bodega to score a few lottery tickets. Serial killers, emblematic of the new violence, killed for pleasure, often momentary pleasure. Some followed demonic voices in their heads. Others murdered to avenge some childhood slight that could never be made right, no matter how many died. Many harbored a mad hatred of women. They all enjoyed their work. They hunted their prey in cold-blooded, reptilian attacks, as if murder satisfied some pre-historic need in them that could be expressed no other way.

There were plenty of culprits to blame for the new violence. The usual suspects — sex, drugs, rock 'n roll – were just more symptoms, not the underlying cause of the pathology itself. The real cause lay with an enormous demographic bulge of young people making their way through the system – the Baby Boomers. Youthful Boomers enjoyed the most secure, most affluent, most care-free adolescent romp in the history of the world. And yet, everywhere they felt oppressed – by the government, by society, and especially by law enforcement.

The Elizabeth P.D. understood, all too clearly, their own limitations in containing the new violence. Incarceration had no effect. Nor did more sympathetic social programs. Criminals just kept multiplying and mutating into more and more cruel life forms. The cops could handle a small minority of miscreants within a law-abiding majority. They could not handle a generational revolution bestirred by the tectonic shifts wrought by the Baby Boomers. Radio cars, nightsticks and extra shoe leather on the beat were no match for an idea whose time had come.

No place suffered more from the new violence than neighboring Newark, which slid farther and faster than anyplace else in the country. (In 1975, Newark was ranked the worst city in America by *Harper's* Magazine using 24 different measures, from violence to park space.) For the Elizabeth P.D., the question — the existential question — was how to meet and stop the disorder of Newark, which threatened its northern border. The cops knew that if they broke, Elizabeth, like neighboring Newark, would be overrun. Deep within their blue souls, in a place rarely visited and never discussed, Elizabeth cops were frightened.

In Meg's hard-headed view of the world, criminals were simply bad guys in need of pursuit and capture. Meg had skipped college in favor of the Elizabeth P.D., so her young mind was unencumbered by any fancy-pants theories about society and its discontents. To Meg, all criminals were just plain evil and irredeemably so. No further explanations were required. If she thought about serial killers at all, it was to drop them into a conceptual box labeled "religion" — theological matters best left to the priests and nuns. Once in the box, they troubled her no more. Unlike many of her fellow cops, Meg felt the Elizabeth P.D. could handle the new violence and they would, in the end, prevail. Beneath her undeniable charms, Meg carried an equally undeniable purpose: to take back the streets of Elizabeth.

Thus came Meg Murphy to be a legend, a much beloved

legend, in the hearts of the Elizabeth P.D.

A little after 11:00 am, Meg and her fellow dispatchers went upstairs to the Police Commissioner's office for their introduction to 9-1-1, the new emergency dispatch system. This was a rare meeting between the top cop of the Elizabeth and the dispatchers who actually ran the place. While the Commissioner gave out promotions and gobbled up headlines, the dispatchers controlled the flow of police testosterone onto the streets. On a busy night, they alone decided whether to upgrade a domestic dispute to a wife beating, a petty theft to a burglary, a bar fight to an assault — all in real time. Unknown to the rest of city, the dispatchers formed the true first line of their civic defense. Meg Murphy represented the best of the breed.

If the Commissioner felt intimidated by the power of the dispatchers over his operation, he did not show it. The top cop sat behind his desk in full dress blues, which he never took off, not even at home. He did not get up. He did not greet them. He met them with the same cop stare he used to clear corners in the North End for 20 years. He opened the meeting in his slow soft voice.

"We're moving to a new dispatch system called 9-1-1," he said. "Anyone, anywhere, who needs help just dials 9-1-1 and they get you."

"So we're changing our phone number?" asked Meg.

"There's more. You and the entire department will be trained in new terms, standard terms, to describe emergencies that require police response. For example, a suspicious person will be called a 10-38, a traffic accident is a 10-50."

"What about a rumble?"

"10-10."

"A drunk?"

"10-56."

"Stolen car?"

"10-99."

As the implications of the new regime sunk into Meg's head, more questions arose in her mind about how this was going to affect her job, and more importantly her status in the department.

"So, the cops are going to have to learn this, too."

"Yes."

Meg was well familiar with the abilities and reaction times of the average patrolman. This new plan seemed to be adding a needless level of complexity to what was already being handled — and handled with aplomb — in her own inimitable way. Her back stiffened a bit.

"How about an ambulance?"

Unable to remember the appropriate code, the Commissioner glanced down at his list. As the seconds ticked by, he seemed unaware of the obvious shortcomings of an overly complicated system to handle such an immediate crisis.

"10-52," he said at last.

The corners of Meg's lips turned slightly up.

"Fire?"

The Police Commissioner returned to his list, pecking through the codes for what seemed a very long time.

"10-70," he said. He looked up at the dispatchers seated around him. They were all wearing the same tiny smile. The

Commissioner realized he was losing control of the meeting, like a street corner gone suddenly sideways. His jaw clenched. His eyes narrowed around a cop stare, a look that said "enough". The dispatchers swallowed their smiles. The Commissioner continued.

"Patrolmen will report back on the accuracy of the call made by the dispatcher. So if you call a guy a 10-38 and he's really a 10-56, we can better evaluate your performance statistically.

"That sounds great for you."

The Commissioner knew all about Meg and her sharp tongue. The street cop in him sensed she was ringleader on this particular corner, and he was tempted to knock her down a peg and thus regain the room. He was also aware of her legendary popularity with the rank and file. He, too, had no desire to get "megged."

"It's more efficient," he said with a tone of finality.

The Commissioner did not have much more to add. He gave them some printed materials to review and a schedule of training dates.

Back at their desks, the dispatchers nervously clucked about the new system, more than a little concerned about having to learn such a new and cumbersome method when the old one seemed to suit everyone just fine. They shared a vague sense that 9-1-1 was an attempt to end their free-wheeling control of the police department and bring them under managerial control. Maybe it was more efficient, but it also imposed a new language between the dispatchers and the patrolmen, a standardized pre-coded language to describe very fluid conditions on the streets they both knew so well, a language that the bosses could now hear.

What do you think, Meg?" asked a dispatcher. The Commissioner is really dug in on this."

Meg was studying her list of 9-1-1 codes.

"10-96."

The other dispatchers scanned their list and found to their amusement that a 10-96 was a mentally disordered person.

"This is going to be a lot less fun," said Meg.

They got back to work and tried to put the new system out of their minds. At some level, they understood that resisting a police officer, especially the top one, was futile. Without another word, they resigned themselves to adapt to the new system and keep their jobs.

"Police department," said Meg to an incoming call from Peterstown.

"There's a cat up a tree outside my house. I can see him from my window."

"You'll be fine," said Meg, knowing full well that every cop in Peterstown was investigating the murder. She disconnected the call.

"What was that?" asked another dispatcher.

"10-83," said Meg.

The dispatcher checked her list.

"Bomb threat?" she said.

"10-4," said Meg, to the general merriment of her crew.

"Going out with Jackie tonight?" asked one of the dispatchers to Meg.

"No. It's Friday. He's out with the boys. I'm working a double."

CHAPTER 6

St. Benedict's

"I see that most of your students are not Catholic."
– The Archbishop.

"Yes, Excellency. But we are." – Father Ed

ather Ed Leahy sat across the broad polished conference table from the Archbishop, prelate of the archdiocese of Newark, and shepherd to some 1.4 million
Catholic souls. The archdiocese covered the most densely
populated counties of the most densely populated state in the
union. The archdiocese included 250 parishes (most of which
supported a grammar school), 35 high schools, 4 universities,
11 hospitals, 3 seminaries and 9 cemeteries, a full service
offering that provided cradle to grave support for the faithful.
Nearly half the population of the territory covered by the
archdiocese was Catholic.

The Archbishop, wearing an official red sash, positioned

himself at the center of his retinue. Lawyers and accountants stretched out on either side of him around the table, encircling Father Ed in a classic pincer formation.

The attacking suits stood ready to prove what everyone on their side of the table already knew: St. Benedict's Prep school for boys, where Father Ed served as headmaster, was doomed. The be-suited men of the Inquisition leaned forward with sharpened pencils, briefs, charts, columns of numbers, and other bits of legal buckshot, anxious to begin their enfilade on Father Ed. The Archbishop, a reluctant executioner, leaned back.

Tall, thin, and ascetic, Father Ed sat with his sole counsel, a young man named Chris Schneider. Chris had recently been accepted to law school but was otherwise without portfolio. He fussed with some papers, looking for something he left back at St. Benedict's.

Founded in 1868, St. Benedict's served the wretched refuse that washed up in Newark from the teeming shores of Germany and Ireland. Much to the disquiet of the native Anglos, the Germans clung to their faith, language, and customs. They drank beer on Sundays. The Irish drank whiskey all the time. The new Catholic arrivals set about building their own churches in the very image of the old world. Their Gothic cathedrals, with stained glass, soaring naves, grotesque crucifixes and gargoyles looked wildly out of place on the sidewalks of modern American cities. Especially when situated next to more spare Protestant houses of worship. Statues, often bloodied and disfigured, stood in every corner and further appalled the iconoclastic Anglos.

The services were equally off-putting. Priests wore ornate vestments unchanged from the time of the Roman Empire. They conducted their services in Latin, a language that few even in their own congregations understood. And then there were the sacraments, hocus-pocus gestures that Catholics believed somehow carried a magical power to save souls. The worst was the Eucharist, scraps of stale bread that the Catholics worshipped and reverently consumed as the actual body of Christ.

Not content to live within existing cities and counties, the Catholics divided up American cities into a competing grid of parishes and dioceses, an ecclesiastical construct left over from the last days of the Roman Empire. To the Anglos, it seemed as though Catholics had a secret plan to govern the entire country after they took it over. A plan, no doubt, drawn up in Rome.

And then there was Pope Pius IX, the anti-Christ himself, who sat atop the entire unholy structure. In the first Vatican Council held in 1869, he ruled that the Pope alone (that would be Pius himself) was preserved from the possibility of error. Speaking from his newly infallible chair, he condemned Protestant heretics, democracy, and material-ism in a syllabus of errors. He also reserved some choice papal advice for the Muslims and the Jews. He further ruled that Catholics were obligated to set up theocracies in countries where they held a majority. These countries would report solely to him. This was the man to whom American Catholics had pledged their loyalty.

The nativists were restless, and with good reason.

In 1868, monarchies owned 70 percent of the earth's surface. The empires of Britain, Spain, France, and Russia were all run by kings, queens, or emperors. So were Germany, China, Africa, and all of the Islamic world. The fledging American republic stood very much alone. Ascendant royalists would like nothing better than to see this dangerous experiment in democracy fail. America had almost destroyed itself in a savage civil war, a much-wished-for fate by aristocrats everywhere. The self-destruction of America would prove two essential facts to the world: (1) all democracies inevitably descended into violent mob rule, and, (2) a propertied class of the best people (such as themselves) was necessary to keep the worst people (such as everyone else) in check.

Many of these old-world royalists were closely aligned with the Catholic Church. The Church of Rome controlled much of the new world, too. To the south lay the entire Latin American continent, brimming with Catholics. To the north, the French Catholic stronghold of Quebec. To the southwest, Mexico was overrun by Jesuits, Dominicans, and Franciscans. In the nineteenth century, even more Catholics poured in from the east into the United States itself. Like all things Catholic, the numbers were alarming. In 1850, Catholics made up only five percent of the total U.S. population. By 1906, they jumped to seventeen percent and formed the single largest religious community in the country.

The Anglos felt that American exceptionalism sprang directly from their Protestant faith. The two were indistinguishable. The popular Know-Nothing party of the 1850's and later the Ku Klux Klan made one thing clear: it was highly doubtful that the American franchise could ever be expanded to include the papist hordes. (No hypocrites, the nativists lived out their faith when they burned down St. Mary's, the Catholic church that preceded St. Benedict's, in 1856.) There was no reason to think that Catholics, with their medieval clergy, their saints, superstitions, and above all, their devotion to the Pope, would ever make good democrats.

The situation looked quite different to the Catholics. Protestants always seemed obsessed with the Roman Church in a way that Catholics were not obsessed with them. Protestants spent inordinate amounts of energy raging against the sacraments, the efficacy of good works (as if hospitals would build themselves), and of course, the Pope. Protestant belief in scripture alone seemed to exclude all other branches of knowledge, especially history.

Protestants thought the world began in 1517 on the day that Martin Luther nailed his 95 demands to the church doors in Wittenburg. For the millennium and a half that came before, the Protestants could imagine no saints, no significant events, nothing really to learn from the ancients and still less from the medievals. It was all just so much superstition until enlightened Protestants arrived on the scene to clear things up. In the Protestant canon, the word of God started with Genesis, skipped antiquity and went directly to the modern age. The Catholic Church took a more inclusive view of history, one that combined classical rationality with Jewish morality, and put the Roman into Roman Catholicism. Yes, the Reformation was unfortunate. But after a century or two, it was filed away with the Great Schism of 1054 between

Rome and the eastern Orthodox Church. Both regrettable, but hardly fatal.

The Church drew in every race and nation from around the globe with a single message of love. The big numbers demanded organization and the Church provided plenty of it. A clerical chain of command rolled down unbroken from the Vatican to every diocese and every parish in every corner of the earth.

Such diversity also demanded doctrinal uniformity. And the Church had plenty of that, too. It was not so easy to craft one moral message acceptable to 100 different cultures in 40 different languages. The Latin language facilitated the conversation across nations and across centuries. An unbroken line of apostolic succession also helped. In 1868, any person could walk into any Catholic church in the world on any given day and hear the same Mass with the same readings in the same Latin language.

In the Catholic imagination, the Mass, essentially unchanged from the time of the apostles, stood at the very center of their faith. During the Mass, the congregation re-enacted the death and resurrection of Christ in a ritual that was both a sacrifice and a celebration, the presence of Christ made real by the consecration of bread and wine. The Mass could not be understood. It could only be experienced as a mystery, like the love of God himself.

Coming from a repressed Europe, the Catholic immigrants were long accustomed to the rule of aristocrats and kings, and, since the French Revolution, dictators dressed up as ideologues. These self-interested classes governed in a manner best suited to themselves. This rarely worked to the advantage of anyone else, least of all the common man. How different was America! In the new world, an average person might live his entire life without bending a knee to an emperor or wetting himself before a warlord. Taxes were light. Formal social obligations non-existent. In the new world, the political class contented themselves with street cleaning and petty corruption. What a relief! The courts and the police existed for a single purpose – to preserve the individual liberties of its citizenry. And *anyone* could become a citizen. America was an idea, not a tribe, a country that existed in the mind, inhabited by those who chose it.

Catholics embraced America with the enthusiasm of a convert. They built churches, schools, hospitals, orphanages, and yes, even dioceses, under the full protection of the law. Catholics fought in American wars, competed in American sports, prospered in American business. Like the Protestants who came before them, liberty begat loyalty. There would be no fifth column of Catholics secretly working to deliver the United States to the pope. Quite the contrary. Energized and exhilarated by the freedoms extended to them, Catholics created yet another American identity, one that proved out the undeniable allure and dynamism of the American system. In the end, both the nativists and the pope were proven wrong. America benefited from a new kind of citizen. The Church benefited from a new kind of Catholic.

Thus came the Benedictine monks to build St. Benedict's Prep (and re-build St. Mary's) on High Street in Newark, New Jersey in 1868.

After the Germans and the Irish came the Italians, the Poles, and the Puerto Ricans — ever more foreign groups who made the Anglos yearn for the good old days of the Irish famine. As upwardly mobile Catholic families left Newark, parents insisted their sons make the trip back to High Street to experience the academic rigor and spiritual discipline for which St. Benedict's was famous.

When the war ended, the neighborhood turned over again, this time to Black and Protestant migrants from the southern states. The sons of St. Benedict — white, Catholic, and management-bound — formed an indigestible lump that stuck in the throat of the Black community. By the 1960's the school had, for the first time in one hundred years, become an alien presence on High Street.

During the 1967 riots, High Street was ground zero for the violence. The young organization men from the suburbs, clad in their maroon uniforms, made inviting and obvious targets on the streets and at the bus stops. In time, the sons of St. Benedict's ceased their pilgrimage back to the central ward of Newark.

Meanwhile, the sixties ushered in the post-modern world. Affluence, consumerism, mobility (and a deep sense of entitlement to all these good things) eroded the faith of Protestants, Catholics, and Jews alike. Vows of poverty, chastity, and obedience appeared quaint to a younger generation that wanted larger doses of money, sex and personal freedom. On this point of materialism, Pope Pius IX was proven to be quite infallible. Vocations declined. Churches emptied themselves. Schools like St. Benedict's closed.

The men of the Inquisition had seen it all before. They cited depressingly familiar statistics about declining enrollment, layoffs, missed payrolls, unsustainable pensions. They shook their heads over the secular, possibly atheist, turn of the country. Without regular injections of cash from wealthy suburban students, the numbers proved that St. Benedict's would slowly circle the drain and disappear as had so many others. Best to cut the losses now, sell the old building to whatever state agency would have it and move on. So said the wise men of the Inquisition.

The case for keeping St. Benedict's open was less clear. The school, had in fact, closed for a year in the confused aftermath of the riots. Many of the monks believed they could not protect themselves, much less their students, from the increasing violence of the streets. Many considered themselves under-appreciated, if not under direct attack, by their neighbors. Worse, the monks felt deprived of their mission. During the closure, half of the monks left St. Benedict's for Catholic schools out in the safer, greener suburbs of New Jersey. As they drove out of Newark for the last time, the departing brothers clung to their bus seats like they were on the last American chopper out of Saigon.

But not Father Ed. The good father led a contingent of monks determined to re-open the school and tough it out on the mean streets of Newark. This he did with donations from the white suburban alumni. These unlikely donors supported a reduced number of local Black boys who could not afford the uniforms, let alone the tuition. Think Bing Crosby without the vocals.

And then there was St. Benedict himself, whispering advice across fifteen hundred years of monastic history about the right and wrong ways to order a community. The Rule of Benedict set down the disciplines and the priorities needed to build a monastery for the ages. First among these priorities was stability of place, a promise to stay where God had set you down. Invoking the Rule, which grew out of the smoking ruins of Rome in 450 A.D., Father Ed and his monks saw no reason to leave the smoking ruins of Newark a millennium and a half later.

In the Archbishop, a social justice warrior and the first of his line to actually live in Newark, Father Ed found a kindred spirit. But the Archbishop also took seriously his vows to maintain the physical and financial health of his large flock. He faced an increasingly difficult balancing act between the white Catholic suburbs and the Black Protestant cities of the archdiocese.

Behind the relentless grind of the Inquisition, the Archbishop had, with great sorrow, decreed the death of many schools and convents in Newark and Elizabeth. With its long, storied history of service and achievement, St. Benedict's presented an especially painful case. It had to be done. But it was a trial for the Archbishop.

Looking down at the sheet in front of him, the archbishop said:

"I see that most of your students are not Catholic."

"Yes, Excellency. They are not Catholic."

The Inquisition harrumphed.

Father Ed paused and considered his next words closely.

"But we are."

The Inquisition fell back as if struck by an invisible bat. The Archbishop reddened to the color of his sash. This uncomfortable truth, served with a generous helping of Catholic guilt, hung over the conference table. Father Ed, was, of course, making the essential point. After a while, the archbishop spoke and made the equally essential, but opposing, point.

"St. Benedict's must close in the fall."

"What if I come up with enough alumni support to keep us going?"

"You won't."

The two squared off in the ancient fight between established churchman and evangelical reformer. Drawing on the logic of the Inquisition, the Archbishop argued his case for closure — rationally, persuasively, implacably. Father Ed uttered a cry of the heart. Picking up the same fight started by St. Peter and St. Paul 2,000 years ago, the two men wrestled across the conference table for the soul of the Church in Newark, N.J.

In the end, there was not much left to say. Father Ed and Chris gathered up their few papers and left to begin the long walk back to St. Benedict's.

"Did you have to get in his face like that?" asked Chris.

"Yes."

"Why?"

"I had to hit them hard.

"That you did."

"We all know the numbers. They don't have the money.

We don't have the money. We have to stop talking about the money."

"They were pretty angry."

"Good. They don't have to say yes. I just need them not to say no."

"You alienated them."

"I needed to make a different appeal."

They pushed on through the still, sweltering air that hung over Clifton Avenue. The late afternoon sun beat down upon them. The burning sidewalks softened the bottom of their shoes. They turned up High Street and ran right into a hot breeze that caught in their throats. Chris went over the numbers again. Not much time left, he concluded, echoing the findings of the Inquisition. Father Ed knew this. He also knew something that the Archbishop and all the men of the Inquisition did not know: the remaining monks of St. Benedict's would never leave. He lived with these men. He knew them. They would never abandon their vow to keep stability of place. He needed time, just a little more time, to keep the Archbishop and the Inquisition at bay. He would make more alumni calls tonight.

Back at St. Benedict's, they parted. Chris got into his Vega and headed out of the city back to his parent's home, where he lived. Chris' father was German. His mother was Irish. Both parents descended from immigrants who had married exclusively within their own ethnic clan. This was not an accident. Chris was the first product of a mixed marriage on either side in 100 years. He wore his blonde hair unfashionably short. He already had the confident look and feel of young lawyer from a good school. Early in the summer, Chris had begun coaching soccer at St. Benedict's as a volunteer. Father Ed found many other uses for him, including legal counsel and consigliere. Today's meeting with the archbishop was pretty heady stuff for an aspiring, but as yet uncredentialed, lawyer.

Chris drove onto McCarter highway and merged into the Friday rush hour traffic. He felt a twinge as he left the city limits of Newark. He wanted to turn around and drive back to the ghetto. Everyone else was running away from Newark like a house on fire (which it literally was). Chris wanted to go back, back to St. Benedict's. Yes, he knew the numbers as well as anyone. But he wanted to join the monks in their improbable mission. He wanted to be in the fight. Father Ed could do that to people.

Chris pulled into the driveway in front of his parent's large center hall colonial home. Lots of cars were parked out front, as you would expect in a house with eight kids, most of whom were driving and living at home. As he walked through the front door, a soccer ball flew past him and onto the front lawn. He walked into the den. Another soccer ball flew over the television, past the lamp and landed on Chris's foot which hovered just above a large bowl of dip.

"Nice save," said his brother.

Chris flipped the ball over to him. He juggled it for a few moments and then passed it to his sister, Annie. She held the ball on her toe while changing the channel of the television.

"Turn on the pre-game for the Yankees," said Chris. "They're playing Boston."

Chris came from a large family of extremely talented athletes and in their house, some sort of ball was always in the air. Each member of their large family excelled at his or her favorite sport, but they all loved soccer. A perpetual game was always in progress in the den. Annie flipped the ball up in the air and kicked a laser shot with her other foot past her little brother to just nick the radiator, which served as a goal.

"Score," she shouted.

The den looked more like a locker room, with shirts, gloves, bats, racquets, and various balls strewn everywhere. The walls were covered with scuff marks from past games. All of the windows had at least one crack. A Nerf basketball net hung on one wall and another one hung opposite it to form a full court, where a two-on-two game was in full swing. A player attempting a drive was crushed against the wall and came up shaking his hand.

"Can you finish?" asked Chris, who had been acting as a referee.

"No, I think it's sprained."

"Need one," said Chris, raising his index finger into the air.

Annie was the quickest to respond. She took up her favorite place directly under the basket, pinned her brother to the wall and called for the ball. The den door opened, and their father announced dinner was served. He nimbly dodged another soccer ball, which skipped into the dining room. The eight siblings followed closely behind it.

The Schneider residence was located in the tony Elmora section of west Elizabeth, the only true suburb in the city. Dr. Schneider and his wife Mary were both born there and

attended St. Genevieve's grammar school together. The good
doctor served in the Pacific in World War II as a Marine corpsman (rumor placed him at Iwo Jima) and played football at
Notre Dame after the war. Once out of medical school, Dr.
Schneider returned to Elmora, married Mary and started his
practice. Their first child Chris soon followed. Still fit at 55,
he cut a tall, formidable figure at the dinner table. Mary was
a quiet, religious woman who grew more serene with every
child she bore. Mary set down the dinner. She said grace with
her fidgeting brood and the meal began with the usual clatter of knives and forks. At least five different conversations
bubbled up at once.

All ten family members were present at the dinner table,
unusual because typically someone was away at school or at
a sporting event. They were seated in descending age order,
with Mary to the right of Dr. Schneider and closest to the
kitchen, and Chris, age 23, and Annie, age 19, to his left.

"You going out tonight?" Annie asked Chris.

"Yeah, the boys are all meeting at the K Tavern."

"Is Jackie going to be there?"

"Yeah," said Chris, "but he's too old for you."

Dr. Schneider agreed. At the Schneider table, there were
two principle topics of conversation: potential romances and
potential education. More specifically, the ways and means
of obtaining both. All of the kids attended grammar school
at St. Genevieve's, the most affluent, most Irish parish in
Elizabeth. After that, the boys attended the prestigious and
high-achieving Delbarton out in Morristown, while the girls
received a comparable education at Benedictine Academy in

the North End.

Chris had been accepted to Notre Dame law school and was scheduled to attend in the fall, the first of many young Schneiders expected to make the trip to South Bend. All of these private schools were financed by a fragile assemblage of loans, athletic scholarships, and capital withdrawn from Dr. Schneider's medical practice. The details of these financial arrangements were openly discussed at the Schneider dinner table. As was the clear expectation that the kids would earn enough pocket money to support themselves.

"What did you do today?" Dr. Schneider asked Chris.

"I went down to St. Benedict's."

"What?"

"To help coach the soccer team."

This required an explanation. It was tough to make any pocket money as a volunteer at St. Benedict's.

Dr. Schneider had attended St. Benedict's before the war. He excelled at science. The monks encouraged him to pursue a career in medicine. He also picked up a working knowledge of Greek and Latin, which helped with his medical studies and generally smartened up his conversation. Four intensely formative years left Dr. Schneider with a deep appreciation of the Benedictine order.

After the Newark riots, when half of the Benedictine monks left the city, their chosen destination was a well-heeled school nestled in the horse country of the western New Jersey. That school was Delbarton. The other half chose to stay in Newark with Father Ed. That school was St. Benedict's. Thus commenced the internecine schism between St. Benedict's and Delbarton, where Dr. Schneider took the side of the upwardly mobile monks of Delbarton. So Chris was working at St. Benedict's for nothing? Really.

"I saw Father Ed today," said Chris. "He says hello."

This required no explanation. Father Ed was a childhood friend of Dr. Schneider. Their friendship had foundered after the schism within the Benedictine order. The two men had not spoken for many years. From Dr. Schneider's viewpoint, Father Ed had undermined the mission of Delbarton, which, along with Notre Dame, was to conquer the world. And worse, it involved the defection of his eldest son to the other side. Such treachery was too close to home and it stirred the marine within Dr. Schneider.

"Father Ed says hello?" said Dr. Schneider repeated angrily. "Anything else?"

"He offered me a job."

"As?"

"Assistant soccer coach."

"For how long?"

"The season."

"What about law school?"

"I'm not going."

The clatter at the table ceased. Dr. Schneider leaned down into Chris's face, snub nose to snub nose. The two of them never looked more alike than when they argued. An identical vein popped out on each of their foreheads in exactly the same place below their identically parted short blonde hair.

"Yes-you-are," said Dr. Schneider deliberately.

"I-want-to-coach," shot back Chris.

Mary reached over and put her hand on top of her husband's. He looked at her and did not see her at first, such was his anger. But she squeezed his hand hard, and he saw her at last.

"It'll be alright," she said.

This was not the first crisis that Mary had defused within her family. Dr. Schneider put his hand on top of hers and took a deep breath. A subdued Corpsman Schneider returned to his dinner as did the rest of the family, uncharacteristically quiet as the gravity of Chris' decision sunk in. Annie reached down to the floor and picked up the errant soccer ball. She began spinning it on the tip of her index finger.

"Does Benedict's give out scholarships?" she asked innocently.

Even Dr. Schneider had to smile at her. The conversation picked up again around the table.

Chris had been secretly volunteering at St. Benedict's all summer. The soccer team liked and respected him. He felt like he made a difference. The law, by contrast, seemed as cold and remote as an Indiana football field in February. The decision to abandon Notre Dame came to him slowly over the summer – then quickly just now at the dinner table with his father.

As the eldest, most athletic family member, Chris embodied the Schneider code, which was to dominate everything they set their eyes upon. He had always carried the Schneider mantle lightly and confidently, a prime example to his younger siblings. He knew his decision would upset the natural order of things as envisioned by Dr. Schneider. He feared the family might consider him a slacker, a person who no longer embraced the Schneider mystique. Chris was relieved to have his secret out, but unsure for the first time in his life of his standing within the family.

"Tell Jackie I said hello," said Annie to Chris.

"He's too old for you," came the chorus from the young end of the table.

"Hey, Dad," said a minor Schneider in a high-pitched, strangled voice, who was relegated the responsibility of answering the phone. "It's Father Ed."

CHAPTER 7

Nugent's

"So what's The Met?" – Bobby

"Turns out it's opera." – Brendan

Nugent's was a cop bar hard by the Newark border. If it weren't a cop bar, it wouldn't be there at all, such was the state of the neighborhood. The native Irish had long ago given up this section of North Elizabeth to Blacks who migrated up from the South in the fifties and sixties. The Irish vacated the houses, but they and their cop friends stubbornly refused to surrender Nugent's, and so it remained an armed camp deep inside Black territory.

During the Great Migration, six million Blacks left the agrarian south for the urban north. Pushed by Jim Crow, pulled by the promise of factory work, Black migrants filled up northern cities just as whites emptied them out for the suburbs. The numbers were staggering. Between 1940 and

1970, the Black population of Newark sky-rocketed from 45,760 to 207,458, while the white population cratered from 383,534 to 168,382. Meanwhile, manufacturers discovered that single-story, horizontal factories in the south worked a lot better than multi-storied, vertical factories in the north. New factories powered by electricity in the south worked a whole lot better than old factories powered by steam in the north. Cheap land, lower taxes and a noticeable lack of unions did the rest. By the seventies, the Great Migration had become a great three-way pirouette, where north-bound Blacks passed south-bound factory managers on the New Jersey Turnpike, and working-class whites stepped back to the suburbs.

In Newark, the new arrivals clustered together in the central ward like so many immigrants who proceeded them. This time, however, there were fewer and fewer entry-level factory jobs to give them a leg up. Instead, they faced a hollowed-out industrial base, dilapidated housing, and a kleptocracy that was out-of-control even by the low standards of New Jersey.

Newark had a long history of corrupt politicians who fed off the private sector. The Italians controlled the city council and the mayor's office. Mayor Hugh Addonizio had a serious gambling problem, which meant La Cosa Nostra controlled him. When the factories left, the trade unions, the mob and the reigning Italian political class decided that it was time to start dining out on the federal government. On the menu: public housing construction.

Federal dollars poured into the pockets of mobbed up

construction honchos and of the pols who steered contracts their way. In the fifties and sixties, the Italian powers-that-be built 46 high-rise projects in the central and south wards, well away from their homes to the north and west. Subsidized by blank checks printed in Washington, Newark constructed more public housing per capita than any other city in the country. The Italian kleptocracy got rich. The Blacks got shoddy ghettoes in the sky built by the mob. The chattering classes in Washington got talking points.

Into this breach stepped the new men of the Great Society, who declared war on poverty, a kind of Marshall Plan for the inner cities. Not a man given to half measures, Lyndon Johnson created the Office of Economic Opportunity and promptly funded it with a billion dollars (back when a billion was a lot of money and not just a rounding error). Sensing their own opportunity, Newark city council members passed an emergency resolution to score the promised Federal monies — twenty-four hours after Johnson won the 1964 election – in a rare show of municipal initiative.

The Office dispensed grants to employ the poor, teach them job skills, and thus relieve poverty. This they did, at least for formerly impoverished political activists like Saul Alinsky and Tom Hayden. This wily pair of fellow travelers obtained large grants, Alinsky in Chicago, Hayden in Newark. They used the money to train demonstrators, disrupt city government and otherwise raise awareness — job skills that would indeed prove valuable in the years to come.

Stirring stuff up proved to be a lot easier than teaching practical job skills, especially since guys like Hayden and

Alinsky had no other skills to teach. To outsiders, it seemed that the grant money was distributed capriciously, often without any discernible pattern. To the insiders, particularly those in Washington, the money followed a clear and consistent path that unerringly found the latest political pet.

In early 1967, using a now-familiar ploy, Addonizio pushed through plans to construct a gigantic medical school that would make him and his fellow council members obscenely rich. The new medical facility would create thousands of new jobs for high-end professionals, but not so many for the poorer Blacks of the central ward. The plan also destroyed 157 acres of legacy housing. The Black community had seen enough. In July 1967, following the examples of Watts two summers earlier, Newark rioted and Newark burned. When it was over, twenty-six people were dead, four hundred were injured and the National Guard occupied the streets. The mayhem reduced entire neighborhoods to charcoal, most of them in the central ward. These neighborhoods never recovered.

The riots confirmed everyone's worst suspicions. Whites blamed Blacks for the violence. Blacks blamed whites for leaving them a corpse instead of a city. And everybody but the media blamed Tom Hayden. The future Mr. Jane Fonda took a victory lap around the smoldering ruins of the central ward and went on to even greater acclaim during the riots at the Democratic Convention in Chicago a year later.

In the nation's eye, Newark looked to be a dangerous, dark place onto which everyone might project their worst fears. Liberals saw racism, Yankee-style, little better or different than racism, southern-style. Conservatives saw a case study of unchecked liberal values, proof that Democratic rule of blue cities led to destruction. Newark became a blunt instrument used by both sides to beat each other senseless. This did little to improve the prospects of the city.

In 1970, Addonizio was convicted on sixty-two counts of larceny and one count of conspiracy. He would serve six years in a federal prison. In keeping with the finest traditions of Newark, this great parliamentarian ran for re-election during his trial. He lost respectably, by a 56 to 44 percent margin, which spared authorities the dilemma of where he might serve out his term.

There were consequences. The riots chased out much of the remaining private businesses. The city lost another 100,000 whites, driving the total population down to 280,000. And still the feds came on with new money for universities, hospitals, schools, and highly paid administrators who skimmed their share off the top. Very little of this white-collar bounty made its way to local Blacks, who were by now enduring their second generation of Federal occupation.

And, of course, more public housing. The high rises had grown so fearsome that even the poorest refused to live in them. The Newark Housing Authority couldn't give them away. City employees took to painting curtains on the apartment windows to give the illusion of occupancy. In 1985, Newark embarked on a *new* urban renewal program designed to clear the slums created by the *last* urban renewal program. By 2000, 40 out of 46 towers were gone.

All of this was hellishly expensive. Expensive for someone, but not for the good residents of Newark. Generous grants from H.U.D. bankrolled the demolition of the old projects and the creation of new ones. Unburdened by any knowledge of local market conditions, the Feds mandated a reduction in rents. This proved unfortunate for the residents because H.U.D. needed tenant rentals to maintain the buildings. The resulting deterioration was depressingly predictable.

For its own reasons, the state of New Jersey got into the aid game and pumped billions into the Newark school system. In 1966, city taxes covered 82 percent of a $62 million school budget. The state picked up most of the balance. By 1991, the city paid 18 percent of a $500 million budget. By 2010, the city was down to 10 percent of a $1 billion budget. Meanwhile, the total population of the city *decreased* from 400,000 in 1960 to 277,000 in 2010.

With fewer students to educate, much of the money went into administration. The system maintained a one to six ratio of administrators to students – twice the already bloated state average and four times the ratio of comparable cities, none of which assured effective management or accurate reporting. The district consistently received the lowest academic ratings the state could give. The high school drop-out rate clocked in at forty-six percent. Ninety percent of Newark high school graduates who attended community college required remedial classes. With seven thousand people on the payroll, the Newark school system ultimately achieved its true purpose, which was to act as the biggest patronage racket in the state.

Even tech billionaires could not resist the call for help.

As part of a public relations campaign to restore his image after the release of the unflattering film *The Social Network*, Facebook's Mark Zuckerberg famously gifted $100 million to the Newark school system — enough to fund its operation for exactly 36 days. That is, if the $ 31 million of the money had not been spent on back pay for the teachers as their price to just sit down at the negotiating table. The rest was burned up by consultants giving PowerPoint presentations to each other. The gift that launched a thousand slide shows was meant to be the first of many bequests to needy school systems across the nation. But after getting mugged by the Newark Board of Education, Zuckerberg quietly shelved his plans to go national.

Outside federal money begat corruption, which begat poverty, which begat violence, which begat a capital flight, which begat the need for more outside federal money. Where the feds found racism, they institutionalized it. Where they found poverty, they nurtured it. Where they found corruption, their money fueled it.

In the Gresham's law of our age, "bad" government money drove out "good" private capital. Juiced by such liberality, the shysters of City Hall scaled up a petty crooked city government into a massively fraudulent welfare state. Criminals ran not just the streets, but the highest councils of city government.

There were not enough grants, loans, and gifts in the world to replace the vanished private sector and the civil society it once supported. Fifty years after the riots, Newark remained a zombie city, a violent, unnatural creature kept alive by outside interests for their own amusement, a social science project gone terribly, but predictably, awry.

Thus came Nugent's to be an armed outpost on the northern frontier of Elizabeth. Most of the seats at the bar were taken by cops, their guns deliberately showing on their belts. Rose, a petite woman of about seventy, sat at the top of the bar. She wore a pair of dress gloves and a matching pillbox hat, neither of which she ever removed, out of her veneration for Jackie Kennedy. A shot of Seagram's gathered dust in front of her. Rose always looked straight ahead at a point precisely eighteen inches away from her nose and slightly up. She never spoke. She never paid. For this, she was considered a legend.

The patrons of Nugent's saw to it that Rose always had a full shot of Seagram's. On a slow night, subsidizing the diminutive Rose might get expensive as she could drink any three cops under the table. But Nugent's was crowded on a Friday night. The cops shared the Rose levy happily and equitably around the bar.

At the other end of the bar from Rose sat Brendan Graham and Bobby Robach, their eyes fixed on the Yankee game playing out above them. It was only 7:30, but the Yanks were already in big trouble.

Both Brendan and Bobby had a similar build – big, strong, quick like the basketball forwards they were in college. They shared an apartment on North Broad Street, well inside the shrinking Irish perimeter. They had also shared Catholic grammar school at St. Catherine's in the North End, high school at St. Benedict's, community college, and ultimately Rutgers. During their college years, they worked together at the GM plant in Linden. At GM, they learned valuable life lessons such as how to eat lunch in the twenty-one minutes allowed before the line started up again. Or not to buy cars built on a Monday or Friday, when the workers were distracted by the weekend, either upcoming or just passed. Or planned obsolescence, GM suit-speak for the lousy cars they made.

Brendan and Bobby also learned that they didn't want to work the night shift on an assembly line for the rest of their lives. They both earned business degrees so that they might one day make their living sitting down instead of bent over a chassis. They studied hard, not out of love for the subject matter, but for the promise of release. A business degree was a passport out of gritty Elizabeth and a ticket to the greener pastures of western Jersey.

Both now worked in entry-level positions in office buildings, where they sat at desks and drank coffee all day, at least that part of the dream fulfilled. They still lived in Elizabeth, but they were only months away from moving out. Their blue-collar fathers — union guys both — called their sons "bosses" with a mixture of pride and loathing. Neither came from a happy home.

"Jackie crashed his Pinto again," said Brendan.

"Where?" asked Bobby.

"Hillside. He just made a right into some guy's driveway. Hit a tree in the front yard."

"He just turned into a driveway?"

"Like it was a street."

"He's not a bad driver. Got 90 on his written driver's test."

"He did signal."

"Maybe he's better on paper."

They both considered the checkered driving record of Jackie Martin as they watched Reggie Jackson strike out to end the 2nd inning. After a lifetime of practice, they were well able to think and talk about anything, even the most complex topics, all while closely watching baseball. It was as if the game, and the entire season, ran deep in their collective subconscious. Not so much separate from the matter at hand as parallel to it.

"You think Jackie's a good driver?" asked Brendan.

"He's a lucky driver."

"Jackson must be down to two-forty," said the sportscaster visiting from the depths of Brendan's baseball id.

"Two forty-four," corrected his play-by-play companion.

"One of these days that Pinto is going to explode."

"On paper?"

"Good point."

Brendan got up to go to the men's room. He said hello to Mike Burke, a lanky classmate with a fang-like smile who had been on the job for several years. Sensitive in high school, Mike had grown a new, tougher skin with the Elizabeth P.D. It protected him from the streets and from his own vulnerabilities. Mike had "turned cop," as the expression went. This meant he worked with cops, ate with cops, drank with cops, and only dated women who liked cops. His new persona screamed out to the world: go ahead and try me. He was, however, a good man to have in Nugent's. The two most recent stick-up artists, both new arrivals from the south, had been carted out in body bags for their trouble.

"We put ten bullets in the last one," said Mike.

"Were you there?"

"Yeah, I got off a couple rounds."

"Hit him?"

"Hard to say. It got busy."

Brendan sensed that Mike, eye-deep in Jameson, was about to go off on a rant, against criminals, against the Black invaders, against the politicians, but really against his father. His old man died at a young age under mysterious circumstances, leaving his mother and him to fend for the family. Mike still lived with his mother and sister in a two-family house on an increasingly small Irish island surrounded now on three sides by an advancing Black tide. This state of affairs did not make him happy, but change would have made him less so. Brendan had heard this all before.

"Gotta go," said Brendan, feigning more urgency than he felt to get to the men's room. When Brendan returned to his stool, old man Nugent was setting him up with another beer.

"I heard you got hit again," said Brendan.

"Second time in three months."

"You keep a gun behind the bar?"

"Sure, but I never use it. I just duck as soon as they pull out their piece"

"Word should be getting around the projects by now."

"You would think."

At that moment, a young Black man entered the bar looking to buy packaged goods. The place got quiet as Nugent walked over to serve him. Turning to leave, the young man saw that the entire bar was watching him silently, or more accurately, watching his hands. The man left and the chatter picked up again, that much louder for the relief they all felt. Mike got up and looked through the curtains to make sure the man had not just been casing the place before making an armed comeback, a common tactic in these parts. Mike signaled the all-clear and returned to his table. The din resumed its manly pitch.

"Must be new in town," said Brendan.

They returned to the Friday night game. Although still in the early innings, it was already clear that the Yanks were going to come up short tonight in a very sloppy game. This required no discussion as their shared baseball subconscious had already conveyed to them how and when it would happen.

"We should get going," said Brendan.

They left their change on the bar and said goodbye to Nugent. On the way out, they spotted super cop Joe Ball, who was sitting at a table by the door. With him was with an attractive bottle blond in a short skirt who was decidedly not Mrs. Ball.

"Hi, Mr. Ball," said Brendan, who stammered a bit, surprised that Joe Ball would cheat on his wife in such a public North End venue as Nugent's. Brendan and Bobby tried not to look at her.

"We're meeting Billy at the K Tavern," said Bobby.

"I heard. He went into New York today with Jackie," said Joe.

There followed a silence in which Brendan and Bobby

both recalled their youth, a time when Joe Ball knew more about their misadventures than did any father in the parish, including their own. He still did.

"Ran into Butch Mahon today," said Joe.

Brendan and Bobby were grateful for the change of topic, away from the girlfriend, away from their shared knowledge of the revelry that was about to commence at the K Tavern, away from this cop who saw everything.

"Where?"

"Broad Street."

"What's he up to?"

"Nothing good. Where's he living now?"

There followed a lively conversation where, in classic Ball fashion, Joe pumped Brendan and Bobby for all the street knowledge they possessed. As always, he disguised the grilling as a charm offensive. So disarmed were Brendan and Bobby that they called him by his first name when they departed, probably for the first time in their lives.

As they walked out of Nugent's, they passed another young Black kid going in. They stopped on the sidewalk and looked at each other.

"Can't be," said Brendan. "Not so soon after the last one."

"What do you think?"

"Hard to say."

They thought about going back to Nugent's to help out in case there was any trouble. Then, an image popped into Brendan's head, an image of twenty armed, testy cops who had been drinking.

"If something does go down, I don't want to be the only

guy in there without a gun," said Brendan.

"Good point."

Their consciences assuaged, they walked across Newark Avenue to Brendan's car, a beast of an Oldsmobile even for 1978. They might have built this very car when they worked together at the GM plant in Linden. Burry Biscuits had just changed shifts, mercifully removing the smell of strawberry Scooter Pies from the air for a few hours. They got into the Olds, drove down Virginia Street, then turned left onto Lower Road.

When they were growing up together in this neighborhood, Lower Road was the dividing line between the white duplexes on the Elizabeth south side and Black Dayton Street projects on the Newark north side. Whites and Blacks both needed this street as a thoroughfare to reach the stores on North Broad Street. By mutual, but unstated agreement, the Blacks walked on the north side and the whites walked on the south side.

The arrangement avoided unnecessary conflicts, but also eliminated the need for any communication between the two communities. The stand-off left everyone just a bit fearful that someone would cross the street and break the peace. Lower Road became a demilitarized zone that served the needs of all. This too, was embedded in the subconscious minds of Brendan and Bobby, several levels deeper than the baseball reel that never stopped, and likewise required little discussion.

"What are we going to tell Billy?" asked Bobby, referring to Joe's girlfriend.

"Nothing."

"That's not going to be easy."

"We don't know anything for sure, right?"

"Good point."

"How's Judy?" asked Brendan, inquiring after Bobby's latest girlfriend. Of the two of them, Brendan was more talkative. More personable, too. Bobby was more taciturn. He rarely initiated conversation and had a tendency to respond in one-word sentences.

"Same."

"I think I broke up with Stephanie yesterday."

"You're not sure?"

"She called to tell me she got tickets for my birthday."

"For what?"

"The Mets. I said 'Thanks, but I'm really more of a Yankee fan.'"

This was understandable. Stephanie was an uptown girl with ideas about art and movies and plays. She could easily confuse the Mets and the Yankees.

"But then she said 'The Met, not the Mets. The Met, you idiot.'"

"What's the Met?".

"My question exactly. Then she got mad and hung up."

"So what's The Met?"

"Turns out it's opera."

"She can't be serious."

"Yeah, she was."

Brendan turned the big Oldsmobile left into the town of Hillside, with its tree-lined streets and slightly larger homes, just across North Broad Street, but a world away from the aspirationally challenged residents of North Elizabeth.

Hillside was less ethnic, less immigrant, more affluent, more – American. They both felt an unspoken relief to be away from their neighborhood with its racial tensions and lower-class ghosts.

"Butch can't stay out on the streets much longer," said Brendan.

"Surprised he made it this long."

They both fell into a disquieting reverie about the possibility of lock-up. Being twenty-four years old, they did not think about what prison would be like for Butch's mother or even Butch, who always lived outside the lines anyway. They could only consider what prison might mean to them, what it would be like to lose their freedom in the screaming prime of male life in northern New Jersey. That thought gave them pause as they balanced their delirious freedom against the sometimes-high cost of that freedom. They had always walked close to the line, but just like on Lower Road, they never crossed over — neither of them. Butch crossed over all the time.

"It'll be a good day when he's gone."

They drove in silence listening to the Yankees.

"Dakota placed," said Brendan.

"I heard."

Both Brendan and Bobby both adored the ponies. Shortly after they learned to read at St. Catherine's, they began to follow the racing pages. They lived for the next hot horse. Evidently, Dakota was not that horse.

"How much?" asked Brendan.

"Grand."

Brendan whistled. Bobby had fallen in love with Dakota
– head over heels, stone mad, Shakespearean sonnet, cut-off-
your-ear kind of love.

"How you going to cover that?"

"Gotta borrow it."

Bobby did not mention that he had already borrowed
money on the street to get the bookies off his back for past
losses. Nor did he mention that Jackie had lent him enough
cash to cover his vig with the loan sharks.

"You gotta quit that horse."

They passed into the still more affluent town of Union, a
true suburb with streets named Pleasant Way, Sunny Street
and Tinkettle Turn and homes — split levels even — that
had swimming pools, barbecue grills and central air. This
was what they really wanted, not just the amenities, but the
security that came with a two-car garage and a large fenced-in
yard. They liked the idea, too, of streets whose function was
to move traffic, not to separate warring camps into no-go
zones. Where streets were just asphalt, not DMZs, and clean,
well-manicured lawns went on forever. Once you got to this
part of America, you never went back to the North End of
Elizabeth. But you had to get here.

They pulled into the lot of the K Tavern and saw a
crunched-up Pinto leaning against a parking meter.

"Jackie's here," they said together.

CHAPTER 8

The K

"Welcome to the K Tavern. Don't be an ass."
– Motto of the K Tavern

The K Tavern was an old man's bar full of firemen and a few young men with old souls. The bar itself took the shape of a half-circle with the patrons sitting on the outside looking at a wall of beer taps, liquor bottles, and television sets. The bartender stood on the inside watching the effects these had on his glassy-eyed customers.

Like all bars, the K Tavern had its own personality, a composite of all the individual personalities that ever graced its stools, some living and some dead, which together made up the nation of K. Certain expressions of long-deceased patrons still circulated around the bar. Their jokes were told and re-told, usually without attribution, for decades. The owner, head barkeep and president of K nation was Ernie, a remarkably unsympathetic bartender with a short attention span who rarely smiled and never drank. Still, under Ernie's steady hand, peace and prosperity reigned over the nation of K. In the center of the bar hung a sign, the revered motto of the bar, which read:

"Welcome to the K Tavern. Don't be an ass."

Ernie was working alone this Friday night. The place was so busy he barely had time to watch the Yankee game reflected in the large picture window opposite the TV. The front door swung open. Brendan and Bobby walked in on a rush of hot July air. Ernie met them with his standard greeting.

"How you dooooin? *Alright?*"

Ernie always answered his own question in the affirmative — just in case you might *not* be alright and wanted to talk to him about it. It was just quicker than feigning interest in the personal problems of his patrons.

Seated around the corner of the bar closest to the door, the section reserved for the young men with old souls, were the Alers. The Alers, the pride of the bar, had recently won their fifth straight championship in the Union recreational basketball league. All five trophies were showcased in a position of honor just to the right of the television. The K Tavern sponsored the Alers, which meant the bar paid for the tee shirts that passed for uniforms. In return, the Alers drank enough beer to put Ernie's kids through college. The Alers were seated in ascending order of age. In the corner by the wall sat Stan, the broad, tall center with glasses and an old-timey George Mikan hook shot. Next to him was Chris, point guard and playmaker, the best athlete by far and the most competitive person on the team. Next came Billy, back-up center and enforcer. Next to Billy was Patrick, a speedy, smallish shooting guard and defensive specialist.

Brendan and Bobby, power and shooting forwards respectively, took their seats on the last two stools. They book-ended the forecourt that anchored the team. Stan, Brendan, and Bobby, with bench assistance from Billy, forged an iron triangle around the basket, impenetrable to unwelcome rebounders and drivers. The team liked to break with outlet passes to Chris who often found Patrick in mid-stride streaking to the hoop at the other end of the court. In a set offense, Chris ran everything, breaking down the defense in creative ways and taking the money shot at exactly the right time in the game.

No one was quite sure how or when they all met, but the first time they played together they felt the team click on every level. They all loved the Yankees, the American League, the Knicks, and Giants, in that order, regardless of the season. Ethnically, they were mainly Irish and German. The Irish blood made them a bit mad, the German reliably so, except for Stan who was Polish and even more inexplicably, a Mets fan. Musically, they had discovered Springsteen early in his career from the time of their mis-spent youth in the bars of Asbury Park. They all wore dark shorts, brightly colored tee-shirts and high white Chuck Taylor sneakers on and off the court, just in case a game might break out. Which it frequently did. They didn't do drugs, not even marijuana. They had all gone through twelve years of Catholic school, which left them with a healthy respect for authority, but enough room for the occasional heresy. Strange for the time, none of them cursed, another legacy of their Catholic upbringing. But they did drink, Exhibits A and B being Patrick and Billy, who had been bar hopping in the City all day with Jackie Martin, player-coach and all-around sixth man of the Alers.

"Where's Jackie?" asked Brendan.

"Passed out in the parking lot," said Patrick.

"Already?"

"Long story."

Jackie Martin was the very embodiment of Alerdom. Deeply cynical but infinitely loyal. A whore's nose for hypocrisy. Irreverent about everything except the Yankees and Bruce Springsteen. More than a little wild. Jackie carried a let's-give-them-something-to-talk-about flair that everyone admired, but never quite duplicated.

Patrick began to relate how he, Billy, and Jackie had gotten into the city around twelve, headed down to the Lower East Side for some lunch, and then began a liquid trek west to the Village. There they reached their final resting point at The Lion, explained Patrick, his long story made longer by nine hours of day drinking.

"Come on, Patrick. While we're still young," said Brendan by way of encouragement.

"On the way home, Billy and Jackie got into it," said Patrick.

"Slap fight?" asked Brendan.

"Yeah, at first."

"It escalated?"

"Yeah. Billy hit him with a right, a roundhouse."

"Knocked him out?"

"Yeah."

"Where were you?"

"In the back seat."

"Wait a minute."

"Jackie was driving."

It took a while for this to sink in. Brendan tried to imagine Jackie and Billy in the front seat having a full-on brawl while Jackie was driving.

"Where."

"On seventy-eight."

"How fast?"

"About seventy."

This took even longer to sink in and when it did, Brendan was impressed.

"So who was driving after Jackie went down?"

"Jackie. He kept driving. Steered us right onto the shoulder and came to a stop."

"He was out?"

"Yeah. Leaning against the door with his hand on the wheel."

"Out?"

"The whole time. Not sure how he did it."

This was the stuff of legends, not that Jackie needed to add another one to his already glittered past. Brendan turned to Bobby

"Did you hear this?"

Patrick repeated the story for the third time and the rest of the Alers leaned in to hear it again.

"That's something you don't see every day," said Chris.

"He's still out?"

"Back seat of the Pinto. In the parking lot."

They all sat quietly, taking in the story, and trying to imagine how Jackie had managed a perfect landing while unconscious. Patrick continued.

"Then a trooper came by."

Patrick had neglected to mention this in earlier iterations, and the Alers leaned in closer.

"Asked Jackie for his license and registration."

"Mother of God!" laughed Stan.

"He got a little testy when he saw Jackie was out at the wheel."

The Alers nodded. This was only fair.

"It's not like we were doing 30 in a 25. We told him Jackie pulled over to switch drivers, which was true."

"Technically," said Bobby.

"Anyway, he let us go. We threw Jackie in the back seat, and I drove us to the K. Trooper took my P.B.A. card, though. I had three corners left, but he took the whole card."

Each of the Alers had P.B.A. cards given to them by relatives and friends on the job. The local custom was for the arresting cop to tear off one corner of the card for each violation before letting the holder go free. When all four corners were torn off, the card would be taken away. When the trooper took the card with three remaining corners intact, he was conveying to Patrick the seriousness of the situation. Still, he let them go.

"Probably right," said Brendan.

They all agreed and mentally checked how many corners

they had left on their P.B.A. cards. In a good year, a card would last ten to twelve months before its owner incurred enough violations to warrant its removal from circulation. Brendan reached into his wallet and produced a shiny, new, fully intact P.B.A. card and gave it to Patrick.

"It's from my uncle if anyone asks."

"They always do."

Every arresting cop noted the name on the P.B.A. card. If the violation was serious enough, he put in a call to the name on the card to collect a deposit for his favor bank. Calls would definitely be made on this one, bad news traveling downhill as quickly as it did. Patrick winced as he re-called the premature revocation of his card. His blue patron, a strict uncle from the imaginary Calabrian village in Peterstown had given it to him only a month ago. He knew that he, too, would have to make a deposit in the favor bank of his uncle, probably something minor, like Yankee tickets, but something. And so the shadow system of justice in New Jersey rolled on, righting the wrongs of its residents, however imperfectly.

Billy had been quietly sipping his beer as he sat through Patrick's retelling of the day, a bit remorseful at having hit Jackie hard enough to almost kill them all.

"How did you make out, Billy?" said Chris.

Billy slowly raised up his massive shaven head to show a bruise on his jaw where Jackie had landed a left.

"But you should have seen the other guy," said Patrick.

They all laughed, Billy too, and he felt his spirits rise for the first time since he saw Jackie go blotto from the round-house. They spent some time going over the story again, asking the same questions at the same points and laughing at the same jokes. When each had finally re-told the story in his own words, they moved onto new business.

"I heard Jackie crashed the Pinto again," said Brendan.

"Yeah, we were coming home from the K on Wednesday night," said Billy. "I was driving right behind him. Made a right turn into a tree."

"I heard he signaled first."

"Yeah, always a stickler." They all laughed. Jackie's checkered driving record was a source of amusement and much head shaking. Billy continued, "We were on our way to the airport."

All of the Alers leaned back.

"Ohhhhhh," they all said at once.

Jackie had a disturbing habit of driving to Newark Airport after a night at the K and booking an impromptu flight to parts unknown. In the winter, he might fly to Florida or New Orleans. In the summer, almost anywhere. The disturbing part was Jackie's ability to convince his companions that they should accompany him. Each of the Alers had, at one time or another, woken up with a hangover in a distant city with Jackie.

"We were going to pick Meg up first."

"They must be getting serious," said Chris.

"Where did he want to go?" asked Stan, still smarting from a recent unscheduled trip to Boston.

"Montreal."

"Ohhhhhh," they said.

"He's branching out," said Brendan.

Each of the Alers made a mental note to never again let Jackie talk them into another midnight mystery flight. But at some level they knew resistance was futile.

"Do you need a passport to go to Montreal?" asked Stan.

Nobody was sure as none of them had ever left the continental United States.

"Probably," said Chris, "but why a National League town?"

This led to a welcome discussion about the current baseball season, with everyone tip toeing around the present difficulties of the Mets, out of respect for Stan and his unconventional sympathies.

"How are Bridget and Mario?" From the beginning, the Alers held a special fondness for Patrick's parents and always called them by their first names. In an era before soccer moms and helicopter parents, Bridget never missed an Aler game. She had taken the time to learn everything about basketball, which did not come naturally to her immigrant sensibilities. But eventually, Bridget learned the art of the fast break, when to press, how to work a referee, which she did often. She was the Alers' biggest and most knowledgeable fan.

Just then, Butch Mahon, who was not a regular, entered the K with two shady-looking guys in tow.

"What are you doing here?" asked Brendan, more out of surprise than civility.

Butch stopped and spun toward Brendan. It took a moment for his rubbery face to snap back into place. He did not at first recognize Brendan so far outside the city limits of Elizabeth.

"Just picked up my boys here. We're on our way back

to Elizabeth. Thought we'd stop in for one. You a regular?"

"Yeah, we play ball for the bar."

"Jackie around?"

"Haven't seen him."

Brendan was not about to tell Butch Mahon and his crew that Jackie was helplessly passed out in the parking lot. Nothing good could come from that. Bobby and Billy, both from the North End and all too familiar with Butch Mahon, gave an indifferent Jersey shrug. Their subtitle read "Do I look like Jackie's mother to you?" None of the other Alers knew Butch, but they caught the chill off their teammates. They sipped their beers warily. Butch ordered a round of beers for his boys and bent Brendan's ear about North End gossip. Two beers in, Butch said:

"Saw Joe Ball in Nugent's tonight. With a broad."

Brendan looked over his shoulder to see if Billy had heard. Billy had his head down deep in conversation with Patrick.

"Shut up," whispered Brendan, nodding toward Billy.

Butch smiled unkindly.

"Whatever you say."

Butch could wear out his welcome faster than a flat beer on a close summer night. Brendan started to look for a way out. President Ernie had been watching Butch and did not like what he saw. Pretending to clean a glass, he walked over to them.

"We're going down to the Barrel House later to beat up some fags," Butch announced.

The Barrel House was the only gay bar in Elizabeth.

"What?" said Brendan.

"We catch them in the parking lot and put a beating on them."

Brendan was shocked. This was way out of line, even for Butch. He looked at Butch's guys. They wore the same mirthless smile as Butch and shook their heads eagerly like the bobble-heads they were.

"We have to wait a few hours till they start coming out. You in?"

Brendan had had enough. It was one thing to talk to a classmate from the old neighborhood, even one as odious as Butch. It was something else to hear, and possibly sanction, such a wanton beating without passing comment. At the same time, there was no reason to pick a fight with Butch and his merry band of psychopaths, especially within borders of K Nation, where fighting was not encouraged.

Ernie leaned over to Butch and said:

"Can I get you anything else?"

Since Butch's glass was full, this was K speak for "I think it's time for you to go." To emphasize the point, Brendan turned his back and rejoined the baseball conversation. The warning shot from Ernie sailed way over Butch's impenetrably stupid head, who loudly laid out his plan of attack on the Barrel House to his gang and anyone else within earshot.

Billy and Patrick were still head down in their own intense sidebar.

"So what do we do about the gun?" Patrick whispered to Billy.

"No idea."

They had discussed the gun, Anthony, and his cryptic

words to Patrick in the garden as they hopped around the Lower East Side with Jackie. That seemed like a very long time ago. It was clear that Jackie was not involved in any shooting and that Anthony was up to something. But what? It was equally clear that they would not be sitting here if the trooper had discovered the gun when he pulled them over on seventy-eight.

"We got lucky."

"Not enough P.B.A. cards in Jersey to get out of that one."

"Still, I'm glad now we didn't get rid of the gun," said Patrick, feeling for the gun butt in the waistband under his shirt for the hundredth time that day. They had considered throwing the gun into the East River, but decided against it.

"I gotta hit the head," said Patrick.

Patrick walked the length of the bar to the men's room at the opposite end of the bar. The entrance door opened. A gust of hot air blew over their backs. Super cop Joe Ball strode into the K. Billy instinctively moved to the men's room and banged on the door.

"Hide the gun," he said to Patrick on the other side of the door.

Joe Ball sized up the little bar. He of course saw his son Billy get up and talk to someone inside the men's room.

"Where's Jackie?" said Joe Ball to Brendan.

"Out in the parking lot."

"No, he's not."

Brendan started to protest, but Joe was already on the move to the men's room. He pushed past Butch and gave his son a hard look. Patrick emerged from the men's room.

Another hard look. Joe disappeared into the men's room while everyone in the bar stared at the outside of the bathroom door. After a few minutes, Joe came out. Hard looks all around. He left without a word.

"He found the gun," Billy whispered to Patrick.

The Alers all turned to Billy for an explanation. The rest of the bar was looking sideways at the Alers.

"Not now," said Billy.

"I'm going to check on Jackie," said Brendan.

The Yankee game ended with a loss for the home team. Both the Yanks and the Red Sox had played terribly, a painful game to watch. Ernie pronounced his verdict on the sloppy, appalling performance.

"It's a shame one of these teams had to win," he said, cleaning a glass.

The entire bar sighed as the broadcasters recapped the game in their Olympian manner, as if they had known from the first pitch that the inept late inning heroics of the Yankees would fall short.

"He's not there," said Brendan, "and the Pinto's gone."

"Let's get out of here," said Patrick.

Two uniformed Union cops in a big hurry walked in. The first one gave the universal upward cop nod to Ernie and held his eye.

"We're looking for Jackie Martin," he said.

K Nation was a fireman's bar, which in no way obligated its citizens to co-operate with their brothers in law enforcement.

"Hasn't been in," said Ernie.

"Let us know right away if you see him."

The cops left. Two urgent visits from the police in twenty minutes was quite a bit of excitement in K Nation and the bar stirred again. Butch had seen enough cops for one day. He picked up his loose change from the bar and pocketed it. Ernie swung by and swept up the imaginary tip with the edge of his hand.

"Don't ever change," said Ernie.

Butch nudged Brendan on the way out.

"Thought you said you didn't see Jackie," said Butch, who heard the exchange with Joe Ball.

"Doesn't matter," said Brendan. "He's gone now."

"Let's go," said Billy.

"Where to?" asked Chris.

It was eleven o'clock. The K would be winding down soon. Patrick and Billy needed someplace where they could speak privately to the rest of the Alers about the gun, about Anthony, about the cloud hanging over Jackie. They greatly appreciated the loyalty that Ernie had shown them, but they did not want him to hear anything that might jam him up later with the local cops. It was best to leave. Then, the youngest man with the oldest soul spoke up.

"How about the golf course?" said Stan, whose boyish curl was now pasted onto his sweaty forehead behind steamed up glasses.

Since the beginning of the summer, the Alers had made a habit of drinking on the ninth green of Galloping Hill golf course after hours. They would park their cars on the street and then walk onto the green with a few six-packs to finish up the night. The Union cops had tried hard to break this habit, cruising by with searchlights whenever they saw cars, usually the same cars, parked on the grass off Fairway Drive. The Aler response was to pile into a single car which they drove *onto* the golf course and parked behind a hill. This suited everyone. The Alers got to drink their beers alfresco without bothering the neighbors. The cops ducked the bothersome paperwork that followed a minor arrest. The very definition of a victimless crime

"Let's go. I'll drive," said Brendan.

The Alers crowbarred themselves, clowncar-style, into the big Oldsmobile and set out for the golf course, only minutes away. Brendan turned onto the golf course and gunned the big steel beast over the hill. The car slid down the opposite side of the hill and came to rest against a large oak tree.

"Maybe we should have picked a different car," said Stan. "Something a little lighter."

Sitting on the ninth green, they cracked their beers. It was one of those Jersey summer nights that got hotter after the sun went down. Patrick relayed the whole story, from nine o'clock this morning to present. Their overheated bodies sucked in beer after beer.

"The cops are definitely looking at Jackie," said Chris.

"He was with me," said Billy.

"When?" said Chris, who cross-examined as if he were still going to law school at Notre Dame.

"The gun was still warm when Anthony passed it to Patrick at ten," said Billy. Jackie picked me up at nine-thirty. My whole family was there, my father, too. I was with him the whole time."

"So who do we talk to?"

The answer was obvious: Joe Ball. He could vouch for Jackie's whereabouts at the time of the shooting. He was a cop. He had the gun. He was clearly working the case in his own way and probably knew more than all of them at this point.

"I'll get with him tomorrow," said Billy.

With super cop in their corner, the Alers relaxed into a contented silence while they processed the events of this momentous day. The moon was full and lit up the golf course. The ninth green looked particularly inviting.

"You got your clubs?" asked Bobby.

"Good idea," said Brendan, who walked over to his car and popped the trunk. He pulled out the clubs and a fresh pack of balls. The Alers divided themselves into teams for a putting competition. More beers and a few games in, they decided there was enough moonlight to move off the green and onto the fairway, about forty yards away, where they played a several rounds of best ball.

Patrick and Bobby went looking for their balls in the tall grass. Patrick found his first.

"Hey, that ball is mine," said Bobby.

"There's no "I" in mine."

"I think there is."

Brendan stuck a tee into the green and was about to drive one into the trees.

"Uh-oh," said Brendan, nodding at the faint orange rim in the east. They all looked over as the morning sun lifted up the night horizon like a sleepy eyelid. As a rule, the Alers tried to make it home before dawn. Normally an intrepid group, the Alers feared the daylight like vampires. Every one of them believed that staying out past dawn caused hangovers, regardless of the volume of alcohol consumed. Getting to bed before sunup was the only way to preserve the next day. It was too late for that now.

"Let's call it," said Chris.

They got into the Oldsmobile. No matter how hard Brendan gunned it, the wheels were stuck in the mud.

"You guys walk back to the K," said Brendan. "I'll figure something out."

The Alers took the remaining beer and headed over the hill between the fading moon shadows that covered the western half of the golf course and the brightening red clouds that lit up the east – a split sky that might have belonged to two different earths.

"Like spirits in the night," sang Patrick from the Bruce Springsteen song of the same name.

"All night," they responded.

"In the night," sang Patrick.

"All night."

"Stand right up and let it shoot through you."

They arrived at the K parking lot. Chris started up his Vega. Bobby, Billy and Patrick piled into Stan's Rambler. They pulled out onto Morris Avenue and headed back to Elizabeth. Sometime around dawn, the fever of the heat wave had broken, leaving a crisp jewel of day. As they waited for the light to change, a shriveled brown leaf drifted down from an oak tree – the first of the season. It spun around and around in slow widening circles, landing softly in the grass divider on Morris Avenue, gentle as an easy death.

The Union County Courthouse on Broad Street.

The Goethals Bridge. Courtesy of Getty.

The Bayway Refinery. Courtesy of Getty.

The Burry Biscuit factory.

The Singer Sewing Machine factory. Courtesy of Eric Williams.

Newark Airport. Courtesy of Getty.

The New Jersey Turnpike. Courtesy of Shutterstock.

Mayor Tom Dunn chatting up a voter. Courtesy of Getty.

John Riggi with lawyer in tow. Courtesy of Getty.

Father Ed Leahy in St. Mary's.

CHAPTER 9

City Hall

"Where was he from?" – Mayor Tom Dunn.

"North End boy." – Police Commissioner

Mayor Tom Dunn sat at his desk and gazed out the window seeing neither the manicured grass nor the brilliant white monuments of Scott Park below him. The heat wave had finally punched itself out. He thought about the good things this might mean for his city: fewer open hydrants, fewer crimes, a less grouchy electorate. Dunn enjoyed Saturday mornings at City Hall, when the empty offices afforded him a rare opportunity to sit alone with his mayoral thoughts. Those thoughts never strayed very far from city politics and the favors, punishments, rewards and betrayals that were the joys of his profession. The mind of the mayor delighted in these things, arranging and re-arranging them like bits of colored glass in a kaleidoscope. Always changing, always changing, the pieces fell in and out of place, forming new and vivid patterns every day, often every hour. But one pattern remained constant: loyalty, a trait he treasured above all on the rare occasions he encountered it. His thoughts settled now on his long-time Police Commissioner, the very image of blue loyalty, who was now struggling against the rising tide of crime in Elizabeth.

As the morning sun spilled into his office, Dunn ruminated upon the many changes that beset his native Elizabeth. Large industrial operations had moved south or simply closed down in the teeth of foreign competition. Even the massive Singer Sewing Machine factory groaned its final death throes down on the waterfront. Middle class whites were moving out, replaced by poorer immigrants from Central America. And then there were the drugs, a new scourge that hollowed out entire neighborhoods in a matter of months and emptied the souls of the next generation. Dunn, an old-time pol who spent most of his nights at local wakes, could not miss the devastating impact of these trends upon the city, his city. Nor could he miss the effects upon his political base.

Dunn was the sole owner and operator of the Dunn Voting Machine Works, an elaborate mechanism of his own creation that converted mayoral favor into votes. Hizzoner provided city contracts, municipal jobs, permits, a short list of hires for the unions that represented the big manufacturers — a blind eye here and there. An appreciative electorate provided the votes.

Alas, the industrial decline had thrown a wrench into the gears of the Dunn Voting Machine Works. Less manufacturing meant fewer union jobs. Less municipal revenue reduced the number of contracts and civil servants. A vanishing private sector left an unfunded spoils system, which threatened the political base of the mayor, and, coincidentally, the city itself.

But Tom Dunn was not without resources. The Dunn Voting Machine had originally been set up to buy local votes in exchange for local patronage. When the manufacturing jobs left town, Tom Dunn raised his sights and sought new opportunities outside of the city. Elizabeth residents, long accustomed to voting the Dunn slate in the city, could now vote for a broader line of Dunn candidates in county and state elections. Grateful politicians in Trenton, flush with cash vacuumed up from the recently adopted income tax, responded with a wide variety of urban renewal projects designed to improve the quality of life for the citizens of Elizabeth — especially the politically connected ones.

Tom Dunn re-programmed the inner workings of his Voting Machine to capture the honeypot of newly available state funds. Instead of union work in the private sector, Dunn supporters now made a living in a wide variety of government projects. Better yet, the new government jobs were under the direct control of the mayor, which allowed Dunn to further tighten his grip upon the electorate. More jobs begat more votes which begat more state grants. Unlike the city's real factories, business was brisk in the Dunn Voting Machine Works.

In the face of economic decline, the wily Tom Dunn became not just a *buyer* of local votes, but also a *seller* of those same votes to state-wide pols.

The feds, too, had upped the ante by introducing revenue sharing, a similar ploy, by which block grants were exchanged for votes in national elections. Lest there be any doubt that Dunn was a motivated seller, the mayor had set up a "Democrats for Nixon" organization in 1972, a feat that assured a steady flow of cash from Republicans in Washington to the heretofore under-loved state of New Jersey. Like any good politician, Dunn understood the inner psyche of his electorate, probably better than they knew themselves. He knew the citizens of Elizabeth to be inwardly conservative people in spite of their outwardly Democratic label. Very few would blame him for deserting a lost-cause liberal like George McGovern. No one did.

The Police Commissioner entered the mayoral suite in full blue regalia with several folders tucked under his arm. The two men had a long history punctuated by a lifetime of deals and promises — some kept, some broken, and some forgotten by mutual agreement. During the Newark riots in 1967, Mayor Tom Dunn issued a "shoot to kill" order, widely credited with keeping the peace in Elizabeth while nearby Newark burned to a crisp. Anyone who knew the Commissioner had no doubt that he would carry out this order. Between the two of them, they had saved the city of Elizabeth from the ruin, flight, and poverty that, post-riot, plagued its big sister city to the north.

But that was then. In the old days, the Commissioner simply followed orders and delivered the blue vote. Eleven years after Newark burnt itself to the ground, the mayor took a long hard look at his Police Commissioner across the table. Dunn admired his ram-rod straight physique, his cold blue eyes, his no-nonsense air. A good man to have in the middle of a riot. But today? With the re-programmed Dunn Voting Machine selling votes as fast as it could manufacture them, Dunn needed his Commissioner to look good in front of the mayor's new customers in Trenton and Washington. These customers took a dim view of old-fashioned cops who shot citizens — even when they weren't rioting.

After some pleasantries, the Commissioner got down to business.

"Murder in Peterstown. Looks like a hit."

"Okay."

The Commissioner continued down his list, barely looking up as he recited the woeful statistics.

"Anything else?" said Dunn, weary of the bad news.

"Hit and run on West Grand last night. Kid died."

"Who was he?"

The Commissioner scanned his list again.

"Jackie Martin."

The mayor paused while he checked his vast internal network of local connections. Unusual for the mayor, he came up empty.

"Don't know him," said the mayor, trying to determine whether he should go to the wake. "Where was he from?"

"North End boy."

"Okay."

The North End was Dunn country. No need to go to this wake.

"He was going out with Meg Murphy," said the Commissioner.

That was different. Reports of Meg's precious *bon mots* delivered over the police dispatch, had reached Dunn's mayoral ears. He had even told a few of them himself. He did not want to get on her wrong side.

"I'll think I'll go to this one," said Dunn.

The Commissioner continued with some better news, which he saved in the hope of ending their meeting on a more positive note.

"We kicked off the 9-1-1 program. Going very well. We expect to see an improvement in police response over the next few months."

The mayor nodded, not so much in appreciation of the crack police work as a welcome talking point, one that sounded something like progress in the face of the current crime wave. In truth, there was very little Dunn could do to stop the citizens of Elizabeth from killing, robbing and maiming each other if that was what they had a mind to do, an unpleasant reality he preferred not to share with the voters. Nine-one-one presented a happy solution, a modern answer to these age-old problems. Best of all, paid for by somebody else, in this case, the state.

"That's about it."

The mayor dismissed his Commissioner, wondering if he should start looking for a replacement after the next election. Dunn was currently negotiating a big deal with the feds, a deal that would bring a gigantic development project to Bayway. He didn't need a trigger-happy Commissioner who reminded Washington of an unhappier time, even if he had just been following Dunn's orders.

Axing the old war horse might even be the first step in crafting a new image, that of a local leader sensitive to the needs of a wider, possibly even a state-wide, constituency. If his Republican patron in Washington could create a "new Nixon", how hard would it be to create "new Dunn"? Then the political kaleidoscope in Dunn's mind turned a bit and he saw his Commissioner in a different, more local, light: steady, much beloved by the blue vote, a vital cog in the Dunn Voting Machine Works. Above all else, loyal. To hell with the feds, he told himself. He would keep his Commissioner.

Next up came Frank Lewinski, the mayor's hand-picked choice for councilman of the 2nd ward and the all-important parish of St. Hedwig's. Dunn barely knew Lewinski, but he liked what he saw: a young lawyer with a chiseled face beneath a head of longish blonde curls. Polish and upwardly mobile, Frank presented the kind of candidate who would appeal to the voters of St. Hedwig's. He would also make them proud. Frank's parents hailed from St. Hedwig's. But they had moved away from the motherland into the Polish diaspora. This put Frank close to Florence Trykta, the little Polish sparkplug who ran the 2nd ward — but not too close. With one phone call, Dunn elevated Frank Lewinski from an ambulance chaser operating on the outer fringe of city politics to a councilman at its very center. Now, the future prince of the city looked at his benefactor with puppy-eyed affection.

"He's perfect," thought Dunn. "Florence will vote him in, but he's mine."

In the kaleidoscopic eye of the mayor, Frank was the ideal choice to oversee the enormous transportation project coming to St. Hedwig's by way of friendly Republicans in Washington: the Bayway Exchange, which promised to connect Elizabeth to the rest of the New York metropolitan area.

Never was there a more inconvenient place to drop down eight million people than New York City. The five boroughs of the city (four of them islands) began as settlements crowded around the magnificent harbor like so many contented frogs around a pond. In the age of sail, the safe, deep harbor gave shelter to larger ocean-going vessels. The surrounding estuaries provided smaller craft with river access to the interior. New York City existed to transfer goods between the two, a happy fact of geography that spurred the growth of the entire region and made New York City the commercial center of the new world. With the passing of sail and the coming of the automobile, these same waterways changed, in the space of a few years, from efficient passageways to impassable obstacles. The boroughs were left croaking at each other like those same frogs stranded across a dry lake.

The metropolitan region responded with no fewer than 20 major bridges and tunnels connected to a one hundred-mile belt of highways that encircled the harbor. By 1978, the belt was completed with one glaring exception: the stretch of Elizabeth that separated the exit ramp of the Goethals Bridge from the entrance of the New Jersey Turnpike.

The Goethals Bridge connected the Isle of Staten (the least populous borough of New York City) to Elizabeth (perennial kid brother to Newark). Connecting the two smallest stepchildren of the metropolitan area proved to be a highly unprofitable enterprise. Built in 1928, the Goethals Bridge still had not paid for itself by 1963.

But all of that changed in 1964, when the Verranzano, the longest suspension bridge in the world, was completed. The Verranzano gave four million Brooklynites dry passage to the Isle of Staten, and by extension, to Elizabeth and the rest of the continental U.S. via the Goethals. Overnight, the Goethals went from being a bridge between two nowheres to a vital link in the Eisenhower national highway system.

The problem lay with the exit ramp of the Goethals, which emptied onto the tortuous streets of St. Hedwig's. Motorists zipping along the belt at sixty miles per hour came to a sudden and perplexing halt as they searched for New Jersey Turnpike signs amid the vowel-deprived names above the Polish delis, garages, and funeral homes of the neighborhood. The promised entrance to the Turnpike did indeed exist. But drivers had to negotiate a warren of local traffic lights, double-parked cars, and side streets to find it.

The Bayway Exchange, arguably the eighth wonder of Elizabeth, connected the Goethals Bridge to the New Jersey Turnpike. The Exchange neatly bypassed the twisted streets of St. Hedwig's and completed the loop around New York Harbor.

As a heartfelt token of their appreciation for the votes fabricated by the Dunn Voting Machine Works, the feds provided the funding for the Bayway Exchange. Happier still, the Bayway Exchange would fuel the Dunn Voting Machine with hundreds of jobs in construction and engineering for years to come. Just in case Dunn did not feel all the love in the room, the feds also threw in money to clean up the running sore of a toxic waste dump under the western terminus of the Goethals Bridge.

In the long run, these improvements in transportation might establish Elizabeth as a distribution center to service the massive retail market in New York City. A new warehousing industry might rise up to replace the conked-out factories of the city. A new day in Elizabeth! All courtesy of the new Tom Dunn!

There was only one remaining obstacle to this sublime result – Florence Trykta. When the Exchange was done, many of Florence's family businesses would be buried under ten feet of concrete and with it, her political influence. Change, most unwelcome change, would indeed come to St. Hedwig's.

This is where Frank Lewinski came in. Frank was to be the face of the Bayway Exchange, a good-looking Slavic face destined to absorb the blows of his countrymen fanatically opposed to the project. Frank knew nothing about the Bayway Exchange, nothing about his role in the coming drama, only that Dunn had lifted him from obscurity to dizzying heights of power. Having spent the morning with Frank, Dunn was now sure of his young protégé, whose face shone with gratitude and blind loyalty, the very picture of ignorant bliss. He would let Frank know about the Bayway Exchange after the election.

"I want you to come with me to a funeral this morning," said Dunn. "Down in St. Hedwig's. There are a few people I want you to meet."

"Sure."

They got up and walked through City Hall together and into a waiting black town car parked in the mayor's spot. The big slant six under the hood pulled the mayor slowly up Broad Street, pharaoh-like. The sun-god Dunn, creator of the eighth wonder of the Elizabeth, waved serenely to his subjects. Whenever the town car stopped at a traffic light, the mayor rolled down the window and chatted up the locals, often by name. They responded with surprise, delight, and almost invariably, affection.

In between lights, Dunn whispered sweet nothings into Franks's ear: promises of higher office, influence, the great things they might do together. This was the full Dunn treatment and the mayor poured it on. Frank floated into St. Hedwig's on a confectionary high fueled by the sugar plum promises made by the mayor, lifted up even higher by his own powdery self-delusions. Frank wanted nothing so much as to be Tom Dunn and if not that – here he gulped a little — perhaps the mayor of Elizabeth someday.

All eyes at St. Hedwig's turned to the stately town car purring in front of the church. Dunn knew how to make an entrance and he chatted idly with Frank while he waited for the crowd to build up.

"You know Florence Trykta?" Dunn asked.

"I heard of her."

"She has a son, Stan, that I want you to meet. He's an up- and-coming kid. Like you. You should get to know him."

"Sure."

Dunn got out of the town car and made his way up the steps. Stopping to shake hands, he soberly but efficiently moved through the crowd in his well-practiced way. The mayor was clearly quite popular at St Hedwig's. Frank followed in his wake, bowing, and scraping in a poor imitation of his new icon and personal savior.

Inside the church, they walked to the front pew that had been reserved for them and sat next to Florence and her immediate family. Dunn gave Florence a slight hug and nodded to Stan, who looked quite pale and not at all well. Stan had awoken just a few minutes before the funeral, but only after Florence had banged enough pots outside his door to wake his deceased uncle resting at the Trykta funeral parlor across the street. He rose and dressed in a highly compromised state, hovering somewhere between the drunkenness of the golf course and the hangover coming at him like the headlight of a distant freight train. Standing in the front pew of the hot and crowded church did nothing to improve Stan's outlook or his appearance.

The service began with a dirge, then continued with the somber, but ultimately hopeful, prayers of the Catholic funeral rite. The deceased was a high-ranking member of the Trykta clan, much beloved by the community. He had spent his entire adult life at the refinery, St. Hedwig's, and the Blue Moon – and nowhere else. The wiry, gray hair that sprouted from his ears was as familiar as the grass growing in the sidewalk cracks of the 2nd ward. He, too, was a physical part of the landscape and he would be missed. The priest, a personal friend of the cold man in the casket, gave the eulogy. He chose several somewhat unconventional, decidedly un-Catholic, lines from W.H. Auden to sum up his feelings.

"The stars are not wanted now; put out every one,
    Pack up the moon and dismantle the sun,
    Pour away the ocean and sweep up the wood;

For nothing now can ever come to any good."
This seemed a bit over the top for most of the congregants, who were more stoic about the long and well-lived life of the deceased. They put it down to the grief of an old man and let it go. The casket inched its way down the aisle and out through the vestibule. The crowd gathered on the steps to watch the pall bearers load the casket into the hearse. Dunn leaned into Florence.

"I want you to meet Frank Lewinski. I would like to run him for councilman in the 2nd."

Florence shook Frank's hand and looked him up and down.

"I know your parents. And your grandparents," she said. "How's your mom?"

There followed a seemingly perfunctory conversation about common acquaintances and idle family gossip. Perfunctory to most, but not to Florence, who took this opportunity to validate Frank's pedigree. Finding no flaw in Frank's blood lines, she nodded to Dunn and got ready to follow the hearse to the cemetery. The mayor intervened.

"Frank, I want you to meet Stan."

Frank and Stan shook hands. The mayor pressed on.

"I would like to see you two work together after the election."

Florence had long sheltered Stan from the political side of her affairs. Although herself a master of the craft, she considered local politics too seedy for her youngest son, the future accountant, and kept him well clear of it. She looked sideways at the mayor, who knew this.

"Maybe I could find you something in City Hall?" said

Dunn helpfully.

Stan looked to his mother, to the mayor and back to his mother. She said nothing. Flattered by the offer, Stan felt compelled to say yes to the all-powerful Dunn. But well aware of his mother's long-standing rule against politics, at least for him, he held his tongue.

Florence had, of course, noted the bridge traffic that now clogged the streets of St. Hedwig's. She knew, too, that St. Hedwig's never stood a chance against the combined forces of the feds, the state, the New Jersey Turnpike Commission, and the Port Authority of New York. Not to mention every disgruntled Brooklynite who found himself sitting on Bayway Avenue wondering what in the world a galobki was. She had heard about the Bayway Exchange and decided that resistance was only useful as a bargaining chip to extract more jobs from the mayor. She weighed the offer, quite a generous offer, in her quick mind. Stan could be more useful to her in City Hall, within striking distance of all that scrumptious federal money, than running a storefront accounting business in St. Hedwig's. Especially if the Bayway Exchange remotely lived up to its expectations. And if the mayor lived up to his. She decided to accept his offer on the spot.

"Something in finance," she said.

At that moment, the hangover express hit Stan with the force of a two-mile train. For a second, he thought he might throw up on the shoes of the mayor. He felt a tremendous pressure building inside his head. Pressure from the mayor, from his mother, from this unwanted career being forced upon him. Who was this guy, Frank? What would they do together?

City Hall? What about his mother's nascent accounting practice under the Goethals bridge? He could not keep up with the
three-dimensional favor game that his mother was playing
with the mayor. Exhausted and dehydrated, he blurted out:

"I can't. I just took a job with Price Waterhouse. In the
city."

Florence turned to her son in a cold rage, furious that
he would abandon her, embarrassed that he would do so in
front of the mayor. She managed to stifle her feelings and
said simply to the mayor.

"We'll talk."

Florence turned and led the rest of the family down
the steps and into the car waiting behind the hearse. Stan,
humiliated that his big breakout moment had failed so badly,
so publicly, followed his mother and her entourage down the
steps. He listed to port like a leaky, unmoored balloon at the
end of a parade: deflated, sinking, about to be left behind.

Frank Lewinski, two parts village idiot and three parts
acolyte to the mayor, turned to Dunn for an explanation.
The kaleidoscope in Dunn's mind shifted again and he gave
a mayoral Jersey shrug. The subtitle under the mayor read:

"Leave it alone."

CHAPTER 10

Newark Airport

"He's gone, Billy. Just gone." – Chris Schneider

Mrs. Ball sat at the breakfast table reading the newspaper. Steam rose from her strong black coffee. Joe Ball, nose-deep in the sports section, listened to his wife recite the crime statistics from the police blotter of the *Daily Journal*, a morning ritual for them.

"Fight in the parking lot of the Barrel House," she announced. "Two hospitalized."

A distant, but growing roar shook the house as a plane landed at Newark Airport. Joe grunted his acknowledgement rather than attempt to shout over the plane. Quietly, Joe registered this altercation into his own internal police blotter, where it was coded, ranked, and stored for future use. Joe possessed an encyclopedic memory for minor crimes. Others might recall major crimes like murders and bank robberies. Joe focused on the small stuff. He could recall purse snatchings, bar fights, petty larcenies from decades past the way some guys recited baseball statistics from before they were born. In the criminal almanac that was the mind of Joe Ball, no crime was minor because it was always connected to another crime. Behind every felony lay a long history of misdemeanors. Joe had dedicated his life to their study. That, and extorting money from the patterns they revealed only to him.

Out on the front porch, Chris' finger hovered over the doorbell. He took a deep breath, closed his eyes and pressed. He heard the chimes, missing a note, alert the Ball family to his presence. Joe got up and walked to the front door. Mrs. Ball gave out a shriek and placed her finger on her place in the newspaper. She cried out weakly to her husband.

"Joe," she said, the color draining from her face.

Joe opened the door and saw a trembling Chris Schneider.

"What's the matter?" said Joe.

Chris put his head down and walked past him. Mrs. Ball looked up at Chris and understood why he was standing in their kitchen at ten o'clock on a Saturday morning.

"Joe," she said softly, her finger dropping from the newspaper into her lap. "It's Jackie."

Chris and Mrs. Ball stared at each other in silence. Tears poured down her cheeks and dripped onto the newspaper, making a patter that beat faster as the tears flowed more freely. A second pool of tears dropped from Chris' eyes onto the floor tiles in-between his sneakers.

"What?" said Joe.

Neither wanted to say the terrible truth. Chris felt

his knees buckle. He held onto the table for support, then collapsed into a chair. His head dropped onto his chest.

"What?"

Chris took a deep breath and raised his head.

"He's gone," said Chris, unable to say more. Joe took the newspaper from his wife and read for himself about the hit and run on West Grand Street the night before. He sat down at the table and read the story over and over, trying to extract some deeper meaning from the cold printed words.

They heard Billy's steps on the stairs. They looked at each other and then turned to the doorway of the kitchen, dreading Billy's arrival, dreading even more the coming exchange. Billy turned the corner and stopped.

"What's going on?"

Now even Joe's eyes were wet. Chris drew a deep breath and tried to steady himself.

"Chris, what are you doing here?" asked Billy.

"Jackie was in an accident last night. After he left the K," said Chris, unable to say more.

Billy looked to his stunned parents. They shared a single open face of grief.

"Is he okay?"

"No," said Chris, shaking his head. "No."

"Where is he?"

"He's gone, Billy. Just gone."

Billy felt something hit him in the pit of his stomach, except it hit him from the inside. The pain rose up through his chest, his throat and then overwhelmed his brain. His thoughts froze for moment, then resumed. "Can't be," he said. His legs weakened and he, too, fell into a chair. He looked around the table, at the tears, at the blank stares. "This isn't happening," he thought. Then he realized he was crying too, unsure of how long. The cop in Joe Ball recovered first.

"What time?"

"Around 11:30. Hit and run."

Out of habit, Joe began to build the crime scene in his head. A slow deliberate interrogation followed about conversations, whereabouts, timelines.

"How did you find out?"

"Meg called me this morning. She took the call from the scene."

"She was working?"

"Yeah."

"She asked me to tell the guys."

"How is she?"

Chris shook his head and closed his eyes as he imagined what it must have been like for Meg to take a routine call about an accident at the end of her shift. And then to discover that Jackie was dead. More tears.

"I didn't talk to her that long."

The mother in Mrs. Ball emerged.

"Do you want something to eat?"

"No."

"Billy?"

Billy was staring into space, unhearing, unseeing. Inside his head, a newsreel flashed from the Vietnam War. He was in it. Jackie was in it, smiling at him.

"Billy!" she shouted trying to snap him out of it.

Billy slowly raised his eyes and wondered why his mother was screaming at him.

Chris pulled himself out of the chair.

"I have to tell the rest of the guys. Meg asked me to."

He put his hand on Billy's hunched shoulder.

"I'll see you later."

Mrs. Ball got up and gave Chris a hug.

"Thanks for doing this," she said.

Chris nodded and wiped his eyes. He had three more stops like this ahead of him. Brendan and Bobby were next over on North Broad Street, then Patrick down in Peterstown. Finally, Stan out in St. Hedwig's. Chris left the Ball house and got into his car.

"Three more stops," he told himself. "I gotta hold it together."

After the shock of Meg's call, Chris steeled himself to carry out her request. He was the leader on the court, the guy who always took the money shot. She knew this and chose him to break the news to the rest of the Alers. He refused to let her down. The Balls were his first stop, and the hardest. In typical Schneider family fashion, he tackled the most intractable problem first. He was relieved to have it behind him. Another deep breath. "Okay," he said to himself, "I got this," and put the key in the ignition.

Billy got up from the kitchen table.

"I gotta get out."

Billy left the house and started walking. He felt as if he had slipped into a dark wet pit that was closing in on him, cutting off his air. He needed to do something physical, anything, to get out, to breathe. And so he walked. Slowly at first, then faster to keep from sliding down any deeper into the pit. With no destination in mind, he found himself at Newark Airport. He watched the planes land and take off for an hour.

Finally, Billy stopped crying. He now turned to the "why" of things. If he had not hit Jackie on Route 78, none of this would have happened. He had almost killed them all. Why had he done that? Maybe Jackie was still groggy from the roundhouse when he drove home. Maybe that was how he got into the accident. Was *he* really responsible for Jackie's death? He needed to walk again, this time to stay ahead of the fiendish devils nipping at the edges of his conscience. He walked faster and faster. He turned away from the airport and headed south on Route One, running at a full sprint.

Fifteen blocks west, on North Broad Street, Brendan parked his mud-splattered Oldsmobile and dragged himself into his apartment building, like a marathoner crossing the finish line — tired, thirsty, exultant. He let himself in and found his roommate, Bobby, sipping a coffee, looking, if possible, even worse for having slept.

"How'd you get home?" asked Bobby.

"Drove."

When Bobby last saw Brendan he was putting on the ninth green at 5 am, pulling on a Camel, his Oldsmobile axle deep in mud.

"How'd it go?" asked Bobby.

"I fell asleep in back seat. Cops woke me up."

"Hmmmmm," said Bobby, rubbing his eyes and bracing

himself for some bad news.

"Asked what I was doing on the green."

"Hmmmmm."

"Told them I didn't know."

"Good answer."

"Told them last night was my bachelor party"

Bobby brightened a bit.

"Nice."

"Told them my friends must have driven me to the golf course and left me there."

"And?"

"They let me go."

Bobby exhaled.

"You gotta be kidding."

"Nope. Even gave me a tow."

"You need to do something for those guys."

"Yeah, I just don't want to get them in any trouble."

"Good point."

They both laughed at their improbable run of good luck. Yet another great escape from the swamps of Jersey.

"Coffee?"

"Nah, I gotta get some sleep."

The doorbell rang. Bobby opened the door and Anthony Fabrizio walked in.

"You look like death," Anthony announced. "The two of you."

Brendan didn't know Anthony. He wasn't in the mood to get acquainted. He got up to throw Anthony out. Bobby grabbed his arm.

"Two large today," said Anthony. "Or $2,500 next week. Your choice."

"I'll have it for you next week."

"I need the vig now."

Bobby went into his bedroom to scare up some cash. That left Brendan, the tall power forward, and Anthony, the short, pudgy, but newly-made man, in an uncomfortable staring match. Anthony won. Bobby returned and handed over the cash. Anthony counted the wad and slipped it into his pocket. He gave Bobby the look of contempt he reserved for his best customers, the same look that drug dealers reserved for their biggest dope fiends.

"$2,500?" asked Brendan, after Anthony left.

Bobby said nothing, but slumped back into his chair. His hungover head dropped into his shaking hands.

"You gotta quit that horse."

"I know. I know."

"What are you going to do?"

"Jackie's been helping me."

"You can't do that to him."

The doorbell rang again. Bobby's face turned a pasty white, fearing Anthony's return. Maybe he forgot something. Like a finger. Brendan opened the door and found Chris standing in the doorway, a small but growing puddle at his feet.

CHAPTER 11

The New Jersey Turnpike

"Gotta keep the peace." – Mayor Tom Dunn

"How about my piece?" – John Riggi

The door of the black town car opened, and Frank Lewinski floated out, high on the laughing gas that the Tom Dunn pumped into him all morning. The chauffer, who had seen the mayor charm and disarm so many others in the back seat of the town car, could not but be impressed by this performance. In the space of a few hours, Tom Dunn had stunned Lewinski, sapped the free will from his otherwise living body and then assigned him a position deep within the Dunn Voting Machine Works, all with his happy consent. The driver looked into the rearview mirror at the mayor and acknowledged him as the master of this dark ancient art with a quick nod.

"Where to, Mr. Mayor?"

"Peterstown."

With Lewinski safely tucked in place, the kaleidoscope in Dunn's mind shifted again as he considered his upcoming meeting with John Riggi, head of the DeCavalcante crime family. Dunn called off his King Tut routine and kept the windows rolled up at the traffic lights. He stared straight ahead and tried to anticipate the many needs of the don.

As always, Riggi wanted money. With the Bayway Exchange, Dunn had much to offer: huge construction contracts for the unions and more than the usual petty slush of payoffs and no-show jobs. And then there was the environmental clean-up under the Goethals Bridge. Both projects could take years, possibly decades, if they played it right. As the business agent for Local 394, Riggi bore responsibility for finding (or creating) new work for his members. The Bayway Exchange promised to make him very popular. And very rich.

As always, Dunn wanted power. Riggi also had much to offer. As the business agent for Local 394, Riggi controlled the membership of the union, which was already well-stocked with friends of Tom Dunn. The union brothers (and their families) voted the line, rang doorbells, and stuffed mailboxes with leaflets that proclaimed the many virtues of the sun-king Dunn. Born and raised in Newark, Riggi was hardly shocked to discover that politicians could be bought. He was always surprised, however, at how cheaply they came, usually for a few votes that were of no value to him anyway.

Dunn took the opposite view. He could never understand why anyone would give away something as valuable as political power for a few bucks. In their many dealings, each man thought he got the better end of the bargain. They got along well.

Dunn's driver double-parked the black town car in front of the Italian-American Anti-Defamation League where Riggi kept an office.

The stubby, ill-proportioned Irishman dressed in his off-the-rack suit entered the club and shook the manicured hand of the well-coiffed Sicilian lord of the manor. The machine meets the mob.

"The Bayway Exchange is going to happen," said Dunn to open their meeting.

"When?"

"Couple of years. But we need to start now. Concrete, steel. Especially concrete."

Concrete, the magic word. Concrete to be supplied by mobbed-up contractors from New York City, people it paid to be on good terms with. A big concrete contract would pave the way of these good intentions.

"I can supply it."

"I need forty jobs in your Local."

This required a good faith effort on the part of Riggi. He would accept the new union members in exchange for the contracts to come later. Assuming Dunn won the primary. Forty jobs placed with the right people could produce 400 votes from dependents, relatives, and other well-wishers, who might also need a job someday. In a tight primary, 400 votes could put the mayor over. The general election was afterthought in this one-party state.

"No problem."

"How about the steel workers?"

"Going to the 2nd ward.

"Trykta?"

"Yeah. Gotta keep the peace."

"How about my piece?"

"There's going to be a big environmental clean-up under the bridge. It's yours."

"Okay."

"You going to run it through the Elizabeth local?" asked Dunn.

"Nah. I'm thinking about getting into the business myself."

This gave the mayor pause. Riggi was suggesting that the mayor steer the huge environmental contract away from the local to his non-unionized self. As a private owner, Riggi did not tolerate featherbedding, no-show jobs, union wages or restrictive work rules. He didn't even force his workers to vote the line. This deal had few votes attached to it. The mayor would receive a cut of the cash, straight-up graft. Cash, not votes, would be the medium of exchange. They had never done anything like this before.

"You can get rid of the waste?"

"Let me worry about that," said Riggi, mentally carving out a quiet spot in the Atlantic Ocean where he would dump the offending materials and pocket the tiresome cost of the cleanup.

The mayor sensed this and pulled back.

"Let me think about it," said the mayor.

The Eagle nodded and moved on to new business.

"There was a hit by the river yesterday," said Riggi. "The

cops are looking at my nephew, Anthony. There's another kid I like for it."

To Riggi's great annoyance, Anthony had botched the hit yesterday on the unfortunate Jimmy Grillo. Anthony had been told — quite clearly: don't talk to the victim, surprise him with a single shot to the head, drop the gun in the river. Instead, Anthony had talked to Jimmy and emptied all six chambers, five in vain. He then gave the gun to a civilian, Patrick Calabrese, in the long-shot hope of pinning the murder on Jackie Martin, yet another civilian. A ridiculous plan. Now Riggi had a mess on his hands. Nevertheless, Jimmy Grillo was dead, as requested. And Anthony needed protection – from the cops as much as his own stupid self.

Fixed contracts, kick-backs, no-show jobs – the electorate would forgive these actions, and possibly even profit from them. Just another day at the office for the sun-king of Elizabeth, New Jersey. But dumping toxic waste in the ocean in exchange for a cash bribe was a bit much. Fixing a murder charge? The voters wouldn't stand for it, not even in Elizabeth.

"I can't help you."

"No problem. I had to ask."

"Okay."

"He's my nephew," said Riggi, in a last-ditch appeal to family values.

"No," said Dunn, who was intimately familiar with the elastic Italian concept of blood relations.

"Okay."

His civic duties done for the day, Dunn got up to leave.

The two pillars of the community shook hands and parted. On his way out, Dunn spotted Joe Ball waiting at a card table for his audience with Riggi.

"Hi'ya, Joe," said the mayor.

Joe Ball, a man of the shadows, was not at all comfortable meeting the mayor at such an infamous crime spot. The non-plussed mayor, with his highly recognizable ride double-parked outside for all the world to see, felt no such scruples.

"How's the family, Joe?"

"Good, Mr. Mayor," said Joe nervously, trying to limit their exchange.

"Glad to hear it."

The mayor left and Joe was admitted to the inner sanctum of the Italian American Anti-Defamation League headquarters.

"How's the investigation going?" said Riggi, referring to the murder of the wayward Jimmy Grillo.

Joe told Riggi that he had appointed himself as chief investigator, a very good thing.

"I recovered the gun."

Riggi was a bit surprised and more than a little impressed with supercop Joe Ball. Nice police work, but now Joe had the upper hand. From Riggi's point of view this could be good or bad. Bad if it led to his nephew, Anthony. Good if Joe could implicate somebody else.

"Where?"

"I found it in a bar in Union. Last night."

"You still got it?

"Yeah."

"Anthony saw a friend of yours in the neighborhood around the time of the shooting. Name of Jackie Martin. We can put him at the scene if you need us to."

Joe Ball paused for a deep breath.

"Jackie died last night in a hit and run."

John Riggi, not a warm man, broke into a broad grin.

"Perfect," said Riggi. "You got the gun. Pin it on the dead kid. Who's gonna know now that he's gone? Who's gonna care?"

"There's a problem with the timeline. I can't sell it."

"Make it work."

CHAPTER 12

House of Patrick

"They let me go." – Mario Calabrese

"What happened to my cigarettes?" asked Bridget, referring to the Luckies that Patrick went out to buy for her yesterday morning. He had returned a day later in the early morning — drunk, singing, no cigarettes. It was clear that he had been on a pretty wild bender. Bridget had no problem with this – only that he had not thought to call and let her know his whereabouts. She was far more worried about him than her cigarettes, but that was her way. Patrick understood this. He pulled himself out of his kitchen chair and rolled out the backdoor. He walked around the side of the house and onto the sidewalk to retrieve the missing Luckies, and a couple of aspirins, from the candy store on Elizabeth Avenue.

Patrick paused at the light on Second Avenue as a big

black limousine rolled by with John Riggi in the back seat, a common enough sight in Peterstown. Not so common was his driver, Anthony. He pointed at Patrick with his index finger in the shape of a gun. He dropped his thumb like the hammer of a pistol.

In Peterstown, it was never good when a mobster pretended to shoot you, even a junior wise guy pointing at you with his fingers. Anthony had passed the warm gun to Patrick just yesterday morning. Today he was driving Riggi around. Was Anthony moving up? For what service? Patrick did not follow the league tables of the mob — who was up and who was down. He would ask his father, who knew these things. Wasn't Billy supposed to talk to Joe Ball today about the gun?

Bridget scrambled up the morning eggs in the frying pan and poured in some anchovies for good measure. She took the gooey mixture and scraped it onto Patrick's plate, along with a piece of burnt toast.

"Are you right, Patrick?" she asked.

"Right as rain," he said without much conviction.

Mario read the sports section of the *Daily Journal* and sipped his morning espresso. There was a familiar noise on the front porch. With anticipation and then pure delight, they turned and watched a white waterfall of mail pour through the slot. There were few things that brought more joy to the Calabrese household than the daily mail. As was their habit, Bridget gathered up the envelopes and distributed them around the table. Bridget put the bills in her pile. Mario lovingly sifted through the advertisements and coupons. They shared a moment of Saturday morning bliss as they read the missives the outside world had taken the trouble to mail to them.

"There's one for you, Patrick."

Patrick opened the letter with the official sounding return address. There he read about a scholarship he had just received to study cinema. A full ride to UCLA, including room and board. Bridget let out a Celtic war whoop and grabbed her son so hard she almost knocked the wind out of him. Mario joined them in a three-way group hug.

"When?" asked Bridget.

"In the fall," said Patrick, reading the good news for the third, but not the last time that day.

They were so happy that they inadvertently sat down on the white plastic covered furniture in the "good room" at the front of the house. The wonderful news sank in. They tried to imagine southern California, the climate, the stars, the chic, the un-Elizabethness of it all. What a place to study the movies! They talked about what clothes to bring, how to get there, all terribly exciting. What would he study? The classics? The post-moderns? Their delighted voices rose all at once trying to be heard. Their squeals stopped people out in the street, who stood up on their toes to try and see inside.

Then, slowly, the hard truth began to set in. This was going to be a one-way ticket. Patrick would not be coming back to make movies in Elizabeth. He would make a life for himself in California. Whatever was out there in California, it had to be good because no one ever came back. Like they were captured by sun-kissed aliens from a perfect, climate-controlled parallel universe. Then came the tears, of happiness, of sorrow, of the inevitable.

Mario reached into his pile and opened yet another official looking letter, this one from Singers, his employer. He blew open the envelope and saw the pink letter inside. He knew he had been fired. He closed his eyes, took a deep breath, and pulled out the notice. Bridget knew, too, without having to read it, that her deepest fears had been realized. Mario read the notice, put it down and confirmed the worst.

"They let me go," he said. "They're shutting down."

Their heads dropped. The pink slip fell from Mario's hand. The unthinkable was upon them. Yes, they had been expecting Singers to close for years. Reduced hours, declining orders, no new hires. Everyone saw it coming, at least in the abstract. But this was real, horrifically real: final, shattering, with no appeal. They did not understand the changing tastes of American housewives and the role that played in the closure of the plant. Or how the Cold War tilted U.S. trade policy toward cheap Japanese sewing machines. Or the coming battles of the financial engineers over the carcass of Singers. They only knew one thing: Mario was an unskilled laborer with a talent for growing grapes in his backyard. And that would not get them very far. Mario would not be the only unskilled laborer on the street. There would be thousands, all looking for something, anything, that might provide some measure of security. Where would he go?

Their mood swung from jubilation over UCLA, to concern, to pity for themselves and then depression. Patrick would be leaving his parents to go to California, never to return. And they would do – what? They owed money on the house, to the grocer, to everyone. Where would they go while he read books about cinema on the beach? Guilt began to roll over Patrick, terrible guilt about his good fortune and their bad luck.

The doorbell rang and Bridget got up to answer it.

"It's Chris," she said.

CHAPTER 13

Elizabeth Avenue

"We have eight kids. It's hard to keep up."
– Dr. Schneider

M eg Murphy lived with her mother and father above the family store on Elizabeth Avenue, just five blocks west of the Turnpike. The store offered a selection of Cuban food, Catholic statues, bits of memorabilia from her mother's native Santa Clara, and a large quantity of American flags thinly disguised as hats, ties, tee shirts and paper weights. The little shop was clean, well-swept and bright, very much like Marie Murphy herself, who ran the place.

The upstairs apartment was a more jumbled affair. The back stairs opened up into a well-scrubbed kitchen, with two bedrooms off to the right and a living room in the front.

Unlike his wife, Rich Murphy cherished disorder. On any given day, old newspapers littered the spaces around his seat at the kitchen table. Dog-eared books marked his favorite places in the apartment, including the bathroom. Unfinished magazines lay open on his side of the bed. But everywhere else, the well-ordered mind of Marie Murphy prevailed. Even the most casual observer could tell who had the upper hand in the marriage by noting the tidiness of the apartment. At the moment, Richard's clutter was confined to a shrinking perimeter around his easy chair – and nowhere else. Marie clearly had her husband on the run. Books and magazines stacked up around his chair to form a redoubt from which Murphy planned to make his last stand.

Even the air in the apartment was subject to competing claims. Richard kept a humidifier humming in the front room. Marie, who liked her air dry and crisp, ran a de-humidifier in the kitchen.

A knock on the door brought Dr. Schneider and his wife Mary into the front room. After some introductions, they all stepped into the Murphy kitchen. When she heard about Jackie's death, Mary cooked up some chicken soup to bring to Meg. She placed a covered dish on the tired counter, worn out by scouring. Marie invited them to sit down for a cup of tea. Richard went to get Meg, who was asleep in her bedroom.

The Schneiders did not know Jackie all that well. He came to the house. He was Chris' good friend. But they could hardly keep up with *all* of their children's friends, a population that grew faster than rabbits during a wet spring. Dr. Schneider did not always like what he heard. Jackie didn't go to college. He drank a lot. He took airplane trips to nowhere. He lived alone in a downtown apartment, a world away from the Schneider's well- appointed parish of St. Genevieve's. He worked at odd jobs – mainly landscaping – all on his own. He was a hustler for sure. Just not a great man who might someday change the world. Just not a Schneider. They knew even less about Meg.

"She's still asleep," said Richard. "I'm going to leave her alone a little longer. It's the first rest she's had."

There followed some civil, well-meaning patter: concern for Meg's health, details about the accident, the shock of it all. The Murphy's clearly liked Jackie. They liked the idea of Jackie and Meg even more.

It was impossible not to appreciate the Schneiders at times such as this. Their obvious sympathy, their strength, their faith, the undeniable fact of their presence here in the kitchen of two people they barely knew – all worked together to comfort the grieving couple. Mary saw a photograph of a young soldier hanging on the wall.

"You have a son?" she said.

"He died in Vietnam. Served with Jackie."

The Murphy's looked down and away to the right, a reflexive tick they both shared whenever their dead son came up.

"I am so sorry to hear that," said Mary.

"They were both posted in IV Corps," said Richard.

"I didn't know that Jackie served," said Dr. Schneider.

"Two years. In the Delta."

Dr. Schneider knew that Richard was a veteran from the way he talked about Vietnam.

"Where were you?" he asked.

"PTO. Marines."

The two marines talked about their service in the Pacific in the quiet, respectful way of middle-aged men who have been to war and back.

Meg stirred in her bed. Whisps of blonde hair stuck to the dried tears on her cheeks. She awoke and for a moment forgot the terrible accident. She did not recognize the unfamiliar voices coming from the kitchen. She recovered herself, remembered, and new tears re-traced the lines of the old ones. She wiped her cheeks and stepped into the kitchen, a much different woman than the one who had fallen asleep five hours ago. Her eyes no longer conveyed the illusion of naivete. They did not convey any illusion at all. They could not. They didn't care to. The Schneiders introduced themselves. She thanked them for coming.

Unbeknownst to Dr. Schneider, his wife possessed a touch of the psychic. She saw and felt dead people, usually right after they died. In time, the dead faded. But their presence could be quite strong immediately after their passing. She now saw Jackie hovering over Meg's left shoulder.

Mary's spirit life remained her secret, a secret that her Greek-speaking hyper-rational husband would have discounted in any event. Mary had come to peace with these spirits. They were rarely angry or even mildly upset about being dead. But they were mournful, unhappy to be apart from their loved ones. This, she assumed, was the reason they still floated about the earth. Over time, the spirits became an extension of her faith. The bereaved sensed in Mary a sympathetic soul, a sympathy that derived directly from her contact with the deceased. She spent a good deal of time at funerals and visiting the grief-stricken. It was in fact her ministry, a ministry that had brought her to the Murphy kitchen today. She watched the ghost of Jackie Martin idly turning some nails over in his hand.

"What did Jackie do for a living?" Mary asked.

"He had a landscaping business. But he could do carpentry, roofing. Just about anything."

Mary nodded. The spirits never spoke to her or even acknowledged her. They always focused on someone else in the room – a child, a spouse, a friend. Meg took a seat at the table. Jackie's ghost followed her around the room, always just a foot away, and settled down directly behind her.

The ghost had Jackie's same short, black hair, the same exaggerated Irish features: a long narrow nose and undomesticated eyebrows. But the ghost lacked the wry smile, the flashing eyes that always saw the next joke coming before anyone else, the wild little glint. That was gone, replaced by a drawn gaze that never left Meg.

"What parish are you from?"

"St. Michael's."

"We're St. Gen's."

The Catholic grammar schools of Elizabeth played each other in basketball and baseball. In the intensely local Archdiocese of Newark, parish rivalries counted for more than national sports franchises. Everyone in the city knew the players and coaches of each school. There followed the usual Catholic rite of naming common acquaintances, teachers, principals, and large families who overlapped each other in various schools and grades, usually no more than two degrees of separation apart.

"You know the Robachs?"

"Sure. Bobby plays with the Alers. Shooting forward."

"Where did Jackie go to high school?" asked Dr. Schneider, who knew it wasn't Delbarton.

"Benedicts."

Dr. Schneider stiffened a bit.

"No college?"

"No."

"Unusual for Benedicts."

"Jackie went right into the service. Started his business as soon as he got out. Had to."

Dr. Schneider cocked his head.

"Dad died."

"That had to be tough," said Mary.

"Where did he meet Chris?"

"Playing basketball. I think they played pick-up together at Benedict's."

Aha, thought Dr. Schneider. So, this was the source of the St. Benedict's infection that was currently raging through his son.

"They were both doing volunteer work."

"What kind of volunteer work?"

"Counseling. Street kids."

Neither Dr. Schneider nor Mary knew about this.

"How long?"

"Long time."

"Sounds like it was important to Jackie," said Mary, her eyes fixed on the ghost.

"Yeah, he loved it."

The Schneiders were clearly not aware of Chris' volunteer work at St. Benedict's.

"We have eight kids," said Dr. Schneider. "It's hard to keep up."

Mary gave her husband a long look that said: You should be proud of your son – he kept this from you out of fear. Shame on you and your ridiculous fight with Father Ed. The doctor, in receipt of her thoughts, nodded his head in agreement. He returned a message that said: You're right.

After a brief awkward pause, the conversation moved on.

"I see you're a reading man," said Dr. Schneider.

"History, mainly."

"American?"

"Yeah."

"Me, too."

There followed another manly conversation about the war, this time from the lofty perspective of armchair generals rather than the grunts they had been in their youth.

"So what do you do?" asked the doctor.

"I work at Singers," said Rich. "I'm a welder. Twenty-five years."

"We're getting ready to move," said Marie. "I've been cleaning up before we go. We're looking to buy this time."

"Almost there," said Rich.

"Where do you want to go?"

"We want to get off Elizabeth Avenue. Away from the traffic. Maybe the North End."

"Wasn't Jackie from the North End?"

"Yeah."

Richard recalled Jackie and a small smile turned up the corner of his mouth – exactly the same smile that Meg had inherited.

"First time we met Jackie was here in our kitchen. He said: 'Why don't you bring in the humidifier from the front room and let them battle it out.'"

Richard and Marie laughed at the recollection.

"So we did."

Now they all laughed, Meg too.

"Who won?"

"I did," said Richard and Marie together.

"Went on for three days," said Meg, who smiled for the first time in 12 hours. "You wouldn't believe the air in here. The kitchen smelled like a dried-out swamp."

A wry smile flickered uncertainly across the face of the ghost, like a light bulb suffering a bad connection from the other side of the life-death divide. Then, the spirit fell back into its sad mask.

The Schneiders got up to go. They knew they would see each other one more time at the wake where the Murphies would return the soup bowl — and probably never again.

The Schneiders walked out through the living room and down the dark, narrow stairs. Past the front door. Past the mailbox containing the letter from Singers that would keep the Murphy's upstairs in their rented apartment for the rest of their lives.

CHAPTER 14

Back to Benedict's

"Tell me about it." – Father Ed

Chris and Stan sat on the red plastic stools of the Blue Moon. Stan chugged a beer to feed his raging hangover. Chris preferred to starve his into submission with a Coke.

"How's Meg?" asked Stan.

"Tough."

When Chris told him about Jackie's death, Stan went blank. Neither spoke for a long time. After that, they exchanged one-word sentences for about an hour.

"When did it happen?"

"Eleven-thirty."

More silence as Stan processed each new bit of information like it was a strange, new-found artifact.

"How's Billy?

"Bad."

With his fourth beer half gone, Stan ordered another one in advance to avoid any unnecessary downtime. A long silence stretched out before them. Stan's eyes locked onto a faraway mirage in an unwavering thousand-yard stare. Finally, he spoke.

"I took a job in New York. With Price Waterhouse."

"I thought you were going into your Mom's business."

"Me, too."

"She okay with this?"

"No."

"When do you start?"

"Monday."

Stan's fifth beer arrived just in time. The walls of his empty stomach rubbed together, further irritated by the beers, which were not having their desired effect. He drank on anyway.

"She wants me to go into City Hall and work for Tom Dunn."

"And you?"

"No. I want Price Waterhouse. I want New York."

Finally, the fifth beer kicked in and Stan opened up. He told Chris about the Trykta family business, the old-world neighborhood built around the soul-deadening culture of the Bayway refinery, his mother, and her shadowy political connections with Dunn. He described his interview with Price Waterhouse, the unlimited opportunities he saw to bring order and sense the world, the life he imagined away from St. Hedwig's.

"I wanted to talk to Jackie about all this at the K. But I never saw him."

When Stan mentioned Jackie's name, his eyes fell back into the thousand-yard stare as if hearing about the hit and run for the first time.

"I'm not going to Notre Dame," said Chris, who then told Stan his own tale of disappointed family expectations.

"So what are you going to do?"

"Coach soccer at St. Benedict's."

"Your father okay with this?"

"No."

In their hungover, twenty-three year old, not-quite-fully-developed brains, Stan and Chris sensed they each had arrived at a decision point at exactly the same moment here together on the red plastic stools of the Blue Moon. They could fall in line with the expectations of their family – or not. They could forge new identities apart from the Trykta and Schneider clans – or not. They might become new, as yet unknown, creations – or not. The next few days would determine everything. One way or another, they were about to grow up.

"I was going to talk to Jackie about Notre Dame last night."

They talked about their Jackie-less future. Jackie always set the pace on the court, the perfect player-coach. He knew who needed a rest, who had the hot hand. He also set the pace off the court: who needed to celebrate, who needed time away, who needed a hand up. That was over. Now, it was just them. As they peered ahead into their adult future, they already missed their youth. The two youngest men with oldest souls talked on for another hour until the silences grew sadder and longer — companionably so.

"I guess we're all on our own now."

Chris got up to go home. Stan slipped off his red plastic stool in search of a bed. In an era before hugging, they shook hands and parted.

Back in his Vega, Chris pulled out onto jammed streets of St. Hedwig's, clogged with Saturday morning traffic pouring off the Goethals bridge. Chris got turned around amid the confused and impatient New Yorkers searching for the promised entrance to the New Jersey Turnpike. He found himself going east instead of west. Lost and without a better plan, he drove up First Street which dead-ended into Singers. Raised in the distant and affluent section of Elmora, he had heard of Singers before, but never actually seen it. He was stunned at the sheer scale of the place: five stories of nineteenth century red brick sitting on 113 acres of waterfront, including its own railroad and dock facilities. Geez, they even had their own fire department.

Chris turned left, drove under the Turnpike and eventually found Elizabeth Avenue. As he passed Peterstown, his mind returned to his short but intense visit with the Calabrese family just a few hours ago. When he told them about Jackie, all three erupted into inconsolable wails. They had no questions. They wanted no answers. They just howled. Chris tried to talk to them, but they did not hear him over their own shrieks. They didn't even notice when he left their miniature white brick house without saying goodbye.

Chris stopped at the light on Elizabeth Avenue and

Broad Street. He looked up at the bright white courthouse, shimmering in the late morning sun. Now that he had given up on law school, it occurred to him that he would never work there as an attorney. He felt a sharp, unexpected – *pang* in his midriff. He took a right onto Broad Street. He passed under the Arch and onto the streets of the North End. He got to Westfield Avenue and checked the time on the bank clock:

11:26

July 22

70 degrees

He finally found the left that would take him home. About to turn onto Westfield Avenue, the steering wheel tugged sharply out of his hands and to the right. Felt like a flat. He pulled over to check. Tires okay. Getting back into the car, the image of Father Ed popped into his head.

"Good idea. I'm only fifteen minutes out."

He bore right onto Newark Avenue and recalled his earlier visit with Brendan and Bobby just a few blocks away. Brendan, without the consolation of sleep for twenty-four hours, had broken down right away. Bobby seemed not to understand a word he said.

He passed Nugent's and Burry Biscuits. Newark Avenue turned into Frelinghuysen Avenue as Chris crossed over from Union County to Essex County, from the free state of Elizabeth to the federally occupied territory of Newark. He heard but did not see the roar of too-close airplanes landing at Newark Airport. The boom of their engines rattled the windows of his car. He passed by the Ball house. Should he stop by to check in on Billy?

"I need to see Father Ed," he thought.

Chris considered the Alers. Would the team recover without their player-coach Jackie? It was hard to tell from their reactions. Billy collapsed into himself like a dying star. Brendan cried. Bobby got quiet. Patrick, Mario, and Bridget screamed. Stan chugged a half-dozen beers and fell into a catatonic state. Hard to tell what it all meant. And how about Meg? She was good on the phone when she asked him to deliver the news in person to the Alers. Very professional. She dispatched him as if he were a cop sent out to handle a family dispute.

And how about himself? He thought again about his own performance this morning and decided that he had carried it well, like the guy who always took the money shot. Like a Schneider.

Chris parked on High Street in front of St. Benedict's. He stepped onto the sidewalk and turned left toward the school to find Father Ed. But he ran into something. Something big. It stopped him short. He looked up and around. Nothing. But still he felt it, like a stiff wind blowing out of the north. No, more like a force field that held him in place. Suddenly, it shoved him to the right, quite violently, toward the steps of St. Mary's. The force field took control of his feet and led him up the steps, into the church to the front pew, where it released him.

"What was *that*?"

Chris did an internal scan of his brain and his body – just to make sure he was okay. Working on very little sleep. Nothing to eat. Nothing to drink but Coke. He nevertheless felt alert, lucid. Check. Mercifully, his hangover had receded and left a trace of loud, clear thoughts running through his head. Check. Emotionally he was drained, but relieved now that all of his morning visits to the Alers were finally over. Check. There was nothing wrong with him. Yet something had pulled him up the steps and deposited him into the front pew. Something that felt like…the tug on his front tire! The same involuntary jolt that yanked the steering wheel out of his hands.

"What *was* that?"

After the strain of the morning and these unsettling out-of-body experiences, Chris took a deep breath. Churches always had that same reassuring aroma. What was it? Incense? Candles that burned a hundred years ago? Re-built in 1857 after nativists burned it down, St. Mary's Church had stood on High Street for 121 years. That's a lot of candles, he thought. He took the cool, agreeable scent into his lungs, then let it slowly hiss out through his lips. He rolled back his shoulders. He relaxed. His eyes followed the wooden arches up to the vaulted ceiling. The church was dark, with a touch of the Romanesque. A lighted golden crucifix hovered over the altar suspended by two thin wires.

So much had happened. The contentious meeting with Father Ed and the Archbishop. Was that only yesterday? He had abandoned Notre Dame, pretty much on an impulse – just eighteen hours ago. The unprecedented split with his father. The big night at the K Tavern. The gun. The cops looking for Jackie. For murder? What was Joe Ball doing at the K? The all-nighter on the golf course. Then, news of Jackie's death.

Meg's request. The soul-draining meetings with his friends on the worst day of their lives. Him as the messenger of death.

Yes, he had been there for Meg. He had shared the grief of his friends, consoled them, absorbed their sufferings. Done the right thing. Done all he could. That part was over.

Now what? Who was left to console *him*? He felt a fresh twist of pain run through his all-too-alive body and mind: the pain of his own loss. I have lost my closest friend, he thought. I hurt. I hurt. I hurt. What about *me*? He had shed all the tears he possessed with his friends. He had none left for himself. He just sat in the front pew alone, dry-eyed, beyond grief, full of pity for himself.

He looked hard at the golden crucifix.

"And what about you?" he accused the mangled body nailed to the cross. "Where are you in all this?"

Chris heard a response, quite clear, quite loud, coming from a place outside of himself. The voice said:

"Tell me about it."

Chris looked up and around. No one there. He looked back at the crucifix. The voice had come from the crucifix. It had spoken to him.

Chris stared at the crucifix as if seeing one for the first time. Chris addressed himself to the man on the cross. It only seemed natural.

"What do you mean?"

This time, there was no response. The crucifix had said all it was going to say.

For the first time, Chris was truly struck by the broken, mangled figure on the cross, the agony on his face. He had seen so many crucifixes in so many churches, in so many homes, including his own. They were everywhere. And yet, he had never really looked closely at any of them. He had grown accustomed, even jaded, toward the pain that man must have endured. Pain far worse than his own.

Still, 'Tell me about it'? What a strange thing to say. And the voice had an accent, a Jersey accent. Not the way he imagined a divine intervention. Not the way it was reported in the *Lives of the Saints*. Not exactly the stigmata.

And then Chris understood the words. The voice was telling him that he, Christ, had suffered considerably more than Chris, Jackie, Meg – all of them for that matter. He, Christ, had been there before and he, Christ, would show him how do deal with his hurt. Because, he, Christ, had already dealt with his level of pain and a whole lot more. Indeed, what *could* Chris tell him about it. Christ already knew.

Chris thought about the events that led up to the crucifixion, a story that had lain dormant in his imagination since grammar school — the passion of Christ. It came back to him now in vivid detail, like seeing the crucifix for the first time. The agony in the garden and the foreknowledge of what was to come. The fearful decision to do it anyway. The show trial and the public derision that attended it. The lies told about him everywhere. The hatred of the mob, so adoring only hours before. The casual and brutal indifference of the Romans. The betrayal by his friends. The abandonment by God himself at his lowest moment, the moment of his death. Physical torture was in some ways the least of it. Chris felt the unrequited love of Christ fill up his own broken heart.

Sitting in the Chapel at St. Benedict's, at the lowest point on the worst day of his life, Chris had come to identify with the crucifixion of Christ. He did not understand why. He still did not understand Jackie's death. Nor the force field. Nor the talking crucifix. None of these things mattered. Christ felt what Chris felt. That mattered.

A hand touched Chris on his shoulder. For a moment, he thought the force field had returned. He turned. It was Father Ed.

"What's wrong?" asked Father Ed, looking at a much different Chris Schneider than the one he had left just yesterday afternoon.

Chris looked up at Father Ed. It didn't seem like the right question. Father Ed sat down beside him. He saw that Chris was unable to speak. He knelt down and prayed with his young friend. After a time, Father Ed sat back. Chris began to speak in a low, guarded, somewhat dismayed, whisper. He relayed the events of the last eighteen hours to Father Ed, who listened without saying a word. He got to the force field and the talking crucifix. He hesitated.

"He's going to think I'm nuts," thought Chris. But he told Father Ed anyway.

"Do you hear voices?" asked Chris.

"All the time."

"Talking crucifixes?"

"Sure."

They talked about Christ and his passion. What it all meant. How it fit. So many questions. Chris felt he was just getting started. He had so much more to learn.

"I can still hear that voice. It's ringing in my head."
Father Ed leaned in.

"When God talks to you," he said, "you don't have to
ask him to speak up.

They talked about the resurrection and how that gave
meaning to the death of Christ — redemptive meaning. How
the resurrection made sense out of his own suffering. As
Father Ed talked, every other concern, every other memory,
every other hope in Chris dropped away. His mind cleared.
Two distinct choices rose up before him. I can deny this pain,
fight it, run away from it. Or I can embrace it, absorb it, let
it work on me. To deny the pain was to suffer in a blind rage
like a trapped beast. To embrace the pain was to transform
himself, just as Christ had done, into a divine being. It wasn't
even close.

"We worship a victim," said Father Ed. "It's the only
thing that makes sense."

Chris nodded. It did make sense. Not in a logical way.
But because there was no other option. He had to embrace all
that was wrong with the world in order to make it right, to
make himself right. This was the meaning of the resurrection.
This was redemption.

Finally, Father Ed, the educator, sensed that Chris had
learned enough for one day. He knew that Chris was tired,
even if Chris did not. They got up and walked out of St.
Mary's onto the street.

"I just heard from your father," said Father Ed. "He's
going to put together an alumni group to help out the school.
It's going to make a difference."

Chris felt a surge of relief. At last, a sign that his father was truly with him, not fighting a rear-guard action on behalf of the faraway kingdom of football in South Bend. They shook hands and parted. Chris opened the door of his Vega and stopped.

"One more thing, Father," he shouted over the roof of his car.

Father Ed paused on the steps of St. Benedict's and turned.

"The voice. The voice of the crucifix. It had an accent. Pretty heavy. Sounded like it was from Jersey City."

Father Ed gave a clerical Jersey shrug. The subtitle under his outstretched hands read: "Tell me about it."

CHAPTER 15

Nugent's Again

"Even Riggi won't dust a cop." – Mike Burke

Nugent's was buzzing. About the shooting there last night. About the murder in Peterstown. About the hit and run that took Jackie's life. But mostly about the shooting in Nugent's.

The Black kid that Brendan and Bobby passed on their way out was indeed the latest aspiring stick-up man to leave Nugent's on a gurney. He had drawn a pistol on Nugent and demanded the contents of the cash register. The cops responded with a hail of bullets.

The shooting at Nugent's brought out the best and worst in the Elizabeth P.D. The best was their commitment to the law, the stone courage that enabled them to take everything the streets threw at them. With restraint. With honor. The worst was the war dance going on over the defense of their tribal watering hole, re-living over and over the last few moments of a lost kid from the projects.

The shooting allowed the cops to claim a rare victory over their ghostly foe – the new violence. The Elizabeth P.D. stopped, at least for one night, the mayhem that threatened the northern border of their city. And it felt good. Good to take real action against their unseen enemy. Good to win a battle, even in an unwinnable war. At least for tonight, the fear of the new violence receded, washed away in a wave of blue triumphalism.

The Yanks had beaten Boston in the first game of a double-header. They were already dominating the second game, which only added to the elation. Rose presided over the racket from her perch at the top of the bar with regal indifference. A big crowd like this would have no problem raising the Rose levy. The cops at the bar, now three deep, warmed to the task ahead of them.

Patrick and Brendan split a pitcher of beer at one of the round tables set up in the corners. Billy had been drinking club soda with a purpose, the same way he usually drank beer, which made him the most hydrated man in Elizabeth. He fingered the straw dangling from his third club soda, like a kid who thinks his peas will taste better if he just plays with them long enough.

All three stared into their drinks. Their faces showed the same trail of grief – denial, shock, mourning, anger. They looked older and as dark as an open grave. They spoke quietly under the din of the crowd. At times they just sat in silence, drawing comfort from each other's sorrow. There would never be another friend to die first. Jackie was it. They all knew that this was going to be a once-in-a-lifetime, singularly dreadful experience. They broke their silence to share an occasional anecdote.

"How about the time he got a speeding ticket in the car wash?" said Brendan.

"I was with him," said Billy.

"How'd that happen?"

"Cop car just followed us into the car wash."

"A real high-speed chase."

"Not exactly the French Connection."

They all smiled at the thought of two cops in hot pursuit of Jackie's Pinto while the underbody of his car received an undercoat of rust proofing, whatever that was.

"Where's Bobby?"

"He wasn't up for it."

The Saturday night shift had just come on across the street at Burry Biscuits. New cookies — peanut butter Gauchos this time – were baking. The sweet smell of Gauchos, both overpowering and delightful, was much beloved in the North End. The neighborhood looked forward to a few days of soft, pleasing aroma – not to mention the opportunity to buy the real thing at the company store, which sold broken cookies to the public at a steep discount. The cycle of cookie production and distribution renewed itself in the North End.

"I caught a break today," said Patrick.

They looked up from their drinks eagerly, hungry for anything that resembled good news.

"Got a scholarship to study film."

"Where?"

"California. UCLA."

"You're moving?"

"In the fall."

Toasts and congratulations all around, glad to see something good happen to a friend. Patrick caught Nugent's eye and gave him the nod to set up Rose with another Seagrams.

Mike Burke, one of last night's shooters, walked over to their table and sat down. He even moved like a wolf. He was working a Jameson pretty hard.

"Sorry about Jackie."

The cops liked Jackie, even though they had to arrest him from time to time. He always carried it well. No disrespect, no tears. As a romantic interest of the legendary Meg Murphy, Jackie held an extra charisma for the Elizabeth P.D.

Joe Ball walked over from the bar. He grabbed a free chair and sat down.

"How are you guys doing?"

"Okay."

"Where were you all day, Billy?"

"Just walking."

Billy told how he walked to the airport, down Route One, all the way down to Peterstown to see Patrick. Out to St. Hedwig's to see Stan. Back again to Brendan and Bobby's place. And now here. In all, he covered thirty miles. The talk turned to the night before at the K Tavern.

"What was Butch Mahon doing there?" asked Joe.

"Drinks with some friends. He was looking for a fight at the Barrel House later."

"When did he leave?" asked Joe.

"Right after you."

Joe dipped into his criminal almanac and retrieved the story from this morning's police blotter, the one about the fight at the Barrel House. Whenever Joe made a criminal connection, a click went off in his brain. He heard one now, a loud one. It had to be Butch. He imagined Butch leaving the Barrel House after the fight – adrenaline flowing, giddy after sending two guys to the hospital and getting away with it, speeding up West Grand Ave. Then he imagined Jackie heading down the same street, coming home from the K Tavern. A crash. Butch screeching away in his car.

"Jackie's accident was 11:30, right?"

"Yeah."

The timeline worked. Joe heard a second click go off in his head. He knew Butch killed Jackie in the hit and run.

"Why do you ask?"

"Never mind."

"What's going on with the hit in Peterstown?" Patrick asked Joe.

In the rush of events, the worries about the Peterstown hit and the gun, the cloud over Jackie had receded to a back story. It seemed a lot less pressing now that Jackie was gone. There wasn't a whole lot they could do to him now anyway.

"I'm still working it."

Patrick remembered that they were going to give Joe their version of the timeline, a version that cleared Jackie of any wrongdoing.

"Anthony handed me the gun at ten o'clock yesterday morning," said Patrick. "The barrel was still warm."

"And Jackie picked me up at 9:30," said Billy. "You remember?"

"That doesn't prove anything," said Joe.

They looked to Joe for an explanation. Joe gave them nothing.

"You still got the gun?" asked Billy.

"I don't have any gun," said Joe, who got up to leave.

This was not the conversation the Alers expected. Joe made it clear that he was not in their corner, that he was working another angle.

"Why do you think Joe has the gun?" asked Mike.

Patrick relayed the events of the previous day for Mike.

"I know he's got it," said Billy. "We don't have it. What's he doing?"

"Maybe he's just playing it close," said Brendan. "Until he knows more."

"Doesn't feel that way," said Billy. "I *do* know the man," he reminded them. "He's working something."

"They don't have any leads in the Peterstown hit," said Mike. "Maybe Joe is looking to give them one."

"Give them Jackie?" said Patrick, eyebrows up, eyes wide.

"Maybe. Whose gonna say otherwise?"

This took a while to process. Jackie was like a brother in the Ball household, and a son to Joe. Would Joe really pin a murder on him? Just to run some street scam? They weighed this possibility against the integrity and character of Joe Ball. Joe came up light. The Alers stiffened their backs.

"Not gonna to happen," said Billy.

"No way," said Brendan and Patrick together.

"So what do we do?"

They felt, suddenly, that they were treading in deep, treacherous waters. Joe was protecting someone, probably Anthony, who was in turn protected by someone else further up the mob chain, probably Riggi. Deep waters indeed. Now the Alers looked sharp, alert. They looked a lot bigger and broader, too, swelled up by their indignation.

"I can bring the true timeline to the *Daily Journal*," said Patrick. "I know a guy who will listen."

"Might be too late," said Mike. "We need to stop this before they name Jackie formally. Once that happens, the system takes over."

"I'll go to Riggi," said Billy. "I'll tell him I know about the gun, Anthony, Patrick. I'll tell him about the newspapers. I'll lay it all out for him."

"He's gonna lay you out."

"I'm doing it," said Billy

"I'll go with you," said Mike. "Even Riggi won't dust a cop."

CHAPTER 16

K Tavern Redux

"Who's siting there?" – Ernie
"Missing man formation." – Billy

Two years had passed since Jackie's death. The Alers never played again. Patrick was back from California and they all decided to get together for a night out. They had not seen each other for six months. The five trophies the Alers won for the bar still stood in a position of honor next to the television, a run that would never be equaled.

Thus came the Alers to sit in the section of the K Tavern that used to be reserved for the young men with old souls. Only they were not so young anymore.

Stan sat in the corner, dressed in a grey three-piece suit and a red silk tie. The boyish curl that used to hang down over his forehead was gone, swept up into the rest of his hairline in a slicked-back flip. His glasses were also gone, replaced by contact lenses. Next came Chris, who was wearing the black non-descript street clothes of a Benedictine monk. Billy had on his uniform from the Elizabeth P.D. Patrick wore a Hawaiian shirt and board shorts with sunglasses perched on top of his sun-streaked hair. Brendan was decked out in sports coat, khakis, and penny loafers. No one wore Cons. They looked like a straight version of the Village People. A chair sat empty between Chris and Billy with a full beer resting on a coaster.

Ernie sidled over and greeted them all.

"How you dooooin? Alright?" he said in his trademark greeting.

"Who's sitting there?" asked Ernie, nodding to the untouched beer.

"Missing man formation," said Billy.

Ernie nodded. He held his eyes down for a moment. He poured himself a beer and raised a toast to Jackie.

"Good to see you all," he said.

In an unprecedented compliment, the tee-totaling Ernie tossed back the beer.

The ghost of Jackie Martin sat on the empty stool wearing the same blank somber expression that never left its face.

Outside, a summer storm lashed the windows of the K Tavern. The warm rain poured down in four-inch drops that swamped the streets. The gutters ran fast but could not contain the waters that overflowed onto the sidewalk. No one would be going anywhere until the hurricane passed. The idea of being trapped in the K Tavern for a few hours pleased them all.

"How's California?" asked Chris

"Pretty good," said Patrick. "Easy to take."

"You seeing any California girls?"

"Trying to see them all."

"Bridget?"

"She's coming out for a visit. She's been reading up on California."

The Alers shared an inward grin, happy to hear that nothing had changed with Bridget.

"Mario?"

They knew Mario had been laid off when Singers closed. He had been out of work for some time.

"He's working on the Bayway Exchange. Cleaning up the toxic site under the bridge. Stan got him the job."

They all looked to Stan, who had given up his big New York City dreams to work for Tom Dunn in the more rustic setting of Elizabeth City Hall.

"Happy to help," said Stan.

After Stan had sobered up, he put off his Monday morning start with Price Waterhouse. With the blessing of Florence, he took an interview with Dunn at City Hall. When their meeting ended, Dunn drove Stan home to St. Hedwig's in the back seat of the black mayoral town car. Dunn had him signed before they got to the courthouse.

Stan's dream to tidy up the earth with Price Waterhouse had died a surprisingly easy death. He rationalized his decision by telling his sensible self that it might be best to start with his own little corner of Elizabeth before he moved on to solve problems of the wider world. At least in St. Hedwig's, he could use his mother's clout to get things done. That it was all good for the Tryckta clan, and what was good for the Trykta's was good for St. Hedwig's and what was good for St. Hedwig's....and so on. That he, Stan Trykta, was an agent of change.

His mother was more practical. She didn't want to be the last person opposed to the Bayway Exchange, especially if the project was already a done deal. Nothing to be gained there. Florence sold her support early, at the top of the market, extracting the highest possible price from the mayor when he needed her the most. She needed Stan in City Hall to keep an eye on all that hot government money that could easily go astray. St. Hedwig's might be changing at last, but Elizabeth politics were not.

The Bayway Exchange had unfolded exactly the way Tom Dunn drew it up, providing the missing link in the beltway around New York Harbor. Westbound Brooklynites — millions of them — passed easily over the Goethals Bridge and onto the New Jersey Turnpike, blissfully unaware of the Polish civilization that lay in ruins beneath them. From there, the New Jersey Turnpike took them to all points of the continental United States. Freight moved in the opposite direction, traveling east from the American heartland to the stores of the New York metropolitan area.

After Florence secured his flank at St. Hedwig's, Dunn wheeled hard at the feds and the Port Authority. He held out for the highest possible price he could get for his cooperation. He got it all: new grants, control over the construction contracts, loans on laughable terms. Just as Dunn foresaw, the Bayway Exchange gave new life to Elizabeth as a distribution center. Warehouses and trucking firms sprang up along the suddenly convenient waterfront. Elizabeth re-discovered itself as a transportation hub with the same happy geographic advantages that first created the need for the city back in 1664. Except this time around, people and goods traveled on asphalt, steel, and concrete rather than water. The Bayway Exchange fulfilled its promise as the eighth wonder of Elizabeth – all breathed into life by the sun-king Dunn.

The feds pumped millions of dollars into the Dunn Voting Machine Works, which rained down jobs upon the just and the unjust alike – as long as they were friends of Tom Dunn. Neither Mario, Bridget, nor Patrick had been political until Stan explained to them the many advantages of voting the line.

"How's the mayor?" asked Patrick

"Strong."

"Glad to hear it," said Patrick, who had a new-found interest in the health and well-being of Mayor Dunn. Patrick continued to vote the Dunn ticket from his residence in the western-most ward of Elizabeth — the Pacific Coast Highway in Malibu.

"How's your business?" Brendan asked Stan.

In addition to his full-time job in City Hall, Stan had opened up an accounting practice. Stan did not service the retail operations of the Trykta clan. Many of those delis and beauty parlors now lay under the Bayway Exchange, their objections muffled in cement like the last cries of Jimmy Hoffa under the Pulaski Highway. No, Stan had only one client: Mayor Tom Dunn. Stan had only one specialty: funneling Dunn's pot of federal cash to his mother who spent it (or withheld it) on jobs, favors and contracts for the Polish diaspora all over the county. In exchange, Dunn received near-unanimous Polish support in local, state, and federal elections. The destruction of St. Hedwig's had done little to diminish the power of Florence Trykta. In fact, the massive patronage that came from her ties to Dunn *increased* her influence in the parish, the wider city, and the county. Exactly the way Florence drew it up.

Over the past two years, Stan had become more interested in politics than accounting. He saw how political power drove people and events in the city. How money shamelessly chased the source of that power. Stan saw how Dunn and Florence built up their machines over the years – often one voter and one favor at a time. How savvy they both were! How subtle the game they played! After securing a few new votes for Dunn (the Calabrese family was his first), Stan developed a taste for electoral politics. He quietly nursed an appetite for more. What was a mere balance sheet compared to the thrill of winning an election?

"Business is good," said Stan, who did not volunteer any more details. He was getting to be as tight-lipped as his mother.

"Thanks again, Stan," said Patrick, raising his glass.

"No problem. There's a primary coming up," Stan reminded him. The Democratic primary! Where the Elizabeth faithful gathered every four years to meet themselves – and were rarely surprised at what they found.

"I'll tell my folks."

Stan nodded. Three more votes in the bag for Dunn. His

mother would be pleased. A pleasant buzz passed through Stan, one that he was starting to recognize: the delightful sensation of having leverage over a fellow human being. Of bending him to your will. The feeling of power. He looked hard at Patrick. Stan no longer saw the speedy little guard who finished the fast break and pressed the most talented opponent all over the basketball court. Stan held in his eye a minion, one who had better vote the line if he knew what was good for him and his parents. Patrick noticed the cold look in Stan's eyes, the unspoken words: I got your father a job and I can get him fired just as easily. Patrick understood and nodded.

"Let me know the line."

"Okay."

"So, Patrick. You working?"

Every time the Alers saw Patrick, he had a different job, none of which they had ever heard of before – assistant producer, creative consultant, visual editor. Each position sounded more substantial than the last, but no one really knew for sure. The east-coast-bound Alers had little idea of the vast infrastructure that lay behind the movie business. The jobs, whatever they were, sounded a lot more interesting than working as a foreman at Singers, Patrick's previous highest aspiration. Sometimes he didn't work at all but was said to be *in development*. When he did work, he was *in production*. Patrick peppered his conversation with fast-moving California movie lingo, like the dialogue of a Quentin Tarantino movie. He seemed quite happy with himself, his new home and his evidently rising career in the *biz*. Patrick had not been to the K Tavern in a long time. When he walked in, it seemed small to him, the way a schoolyard looks to a grown man who returns after many years.

"I got a new job as a production assistant. In animation."

Animation.

"What's that, cartoons?"

"Sort of. More than that. Now they can create digital backdrops without going on location."

Digital backdrops.

"It's a lot less expensive. Someday they're even going to be able to create actors — avatars — right in the studio.

Avatars.

"It's all hi-tech," said Patrick.

Hi-tech.

To the Alers, raised on *Star Trek* and *The Jetsons*, technology meant space travel. Not something you did down here on earth, let alone in the intensely analog state of New Jersey. In 1978, no one had ever heard of the personal computer. Or Bill Gates, who was 23. Or Steve Jobs, who was 24. By 1980, they were about to find out.

After so many decades lost to stagflation, gas lines, near permanent recession, factory closures, little investment and no returns, a handful of Americans living on the west coast had come up with a few ideas. Like the microprocessor, relational databases, the mouse, fiber optic cable, the internet and ultimately the cell phone, all linked together by software – the new technology. The new technology could both consume and produce content on an epic scale. More content drove the need for more processing power, which drove the need for more storage, which drove the need for more fiber and software. Not unlike the symbiotic relationship between coal and the railroads that drove the growth of the country in the previous century. Except this time, the product was not coal nor crops nor steel. This time, the product lay within people's minds. This time, the new technology reached into people's imagination, extracted the content within, and put it up for sale in a global marketplace – right alongside their deepest fears and aspirations. Idea formation, not capital formation, would drive this revolution.

The new technology thrived in the spontaneous culture of the Baby Boomers. To the surprise of exactly *no one*, American Baby Boomers embraced the new technology, which pushed their vision of radical personal freedom to new, unimagined heights. With personal computers, personal phones, personal newsfeeds and personal playlists. To the surprise of *everyone*, the Boomers displayed an instinct for tech capitalism – an instinct that had been nowhere in evidence at Woodstock. The Boomers played the new technology like a Jimi Hendrix riff: creative, self-absorbed, technically superb.

Within a remarkably short time, the new technology remade entire industries. Banks and accounting departments abandoned workpapers, hand calculators, and pencils (and lots of erasers) in favor of electronic spreadsheets. E-mail replaced paper. Word processing software replaced typists. With the Walkman, the world took its first few faltering steps toward mobile computing. New consumer gadgets grabbed the headlines. But deeper changes were taking place in less heralded industries, such as manufacturing.

"Technology is killing the refinery," said Stan.

"How so?"

"Robots. More coming on every day. They're cutting jobs everywhere. Then there's the Colonial Pipeline."

The Colonial Pipeline. A 36-inch band of steel that started in Texas and ended in New Jersey, just a few miles away from the Bayway Refinery. The digitally enabled Colonial Pipeline delivered finished gasoline that effectively undercut the high-cost output of the Bayway Refinery. The refinery and the pipeline engaged in a death struggle for control of the New York metropolitan market. The pipeline, the latest technological innovation from the west, was winning out. The 70-year-old monopoly created by John Rockefeller was failing.

The little Polish enclave of St. Hedwig's suffered the worst effects of the new technology. Lots of blue-collar jobs lost. Lots of quiet cash registers. Lots of empty red plastic stools at The Blue Moon.

There were a few consolations, however. The new technology could not thrive within closed Communist societies. The Soviet Union got left behind like a cranky IBM 360: hard-coded, inflexible, heavily dependent upon an entrenched class of gate keepers who added little value. Free-born Americans tapping away at their keyboards eroded the hegemony of the Soviets as much as U.S. boots and missiles, perhaps more. The reduced Soviet threat was welcome at St. Hedwig's, which, along with the refinery, had doubled as a Russian nuclear target. Still, they would have preferred to get their old jobs back.

"How's Bobby?"

"I haven't seen him in a while," said Brendan. Not since

I moved out. He dropped out of sight. Right after Jackie died."

"Is he Okay?"

"Can't really say. He just stopped coming around. I think he's still in the apartment on North Broad Street."

Brendan and Bobby had been inseparable all of their lives. It was hard to imagine them apart. But there it was. Brendan did not mention the gambling addiction that had consumed Bobby and cost him his job. Nor did he mention that Jackie had been carrying Bobby's losses. Nor that after Jackie died, Bobby was reduced to the status of a pack animal on the DeCavalcante manor. Brendan couldn't watch it anymore. He had to move out.

"I just got engaged," said Brendan.

"When?"

"Yesterday. Wedding scheduled for the spring. You're all invited."

Congratulations all around. This was expected. After Jackie died, Brendan had gone hard for Stephanie. They were closer than doves.

"We're going to the Met tomorrow night."

"The Mets?" asked Stan hopefully.

"No. The *Met*. It's opera."

"I think I knew that."

When Jackie died and Brendan took up more seriously with Stephanie, the taciturn Bobby withdrew from the Alers. Without the routine of regular games, it became easy to let him fall away from the group. Not without regrets, but easy all the same. Nobody planned it or wanted it, but nobody stopped it either.

"We finally got Anthony for the Peterstown hit," said Billy.
"About time."

Billy, Patrick, and Mike had indeed paid a visit to John
Riggi. They had indeed laid it all out for Riggi, who quietly
backed off his plan to frame Jackie for the murder. Anthony
had indeed been caught, tried, and convicted, with convincing
testimony from Billy and Patrick.

"Whatever happened with the gun?"

"It was Anthony's."

"So Jackie's been cleared?"

"Yeah," said Billy. His face hardened around a cop stare.

Billy never forgave himself for Jackie's death. Billy
would not — could not — stop the reel of "what-ifs" that
ran through his head. Hundreds of them. "What if" he had
not thrown the roundhouse that took out Jackie on Route
78? Jackie would have joined them on the golf course instead
of dying in a wreck on West Grand Street. "What if" they
had not drunk so much beer that day in New York? They
might have had a quiet night at the K watching the Yankees.
Maybe a few less beers and Jackie would still be alive. Maybe
just one less beer. "What if" his father had arrested Butch
in the hot Caddy on Broad Street that Friday morning in
front of the courthouse? Butch might have been sitting in jail
instead of plowing into Jackie's Pinto 15 hours later. The reel
of alternative endings flickered through Billy's mind like a
marathon of horror movies. And in every one of them, Jackie
walked out alive. His friends and family assured him that
he was not to blame. But their words had no effect. After a
while, everybody stopped trying.

Billy had never taken another drink after Jackie's death. In his waking mind, the thought of drinking beer filled him with guilt, and even a touch of nausea. In his sleeping mind, he feared the loss of control and the resulting physical damage he might inflict. Like the single roundhouse that had changed everything. However, he still loved the smell of bars. He drank glass after glass of club soda with his old resolve.

"We got Butch Mahon, too."

"You got him for Jackie's hit and run?"

"Yeah," said Billy. "And a few other things."

They all knew that Butch had stood trial for the hit and run that killed Jackie. Their eyes pinched in anger, and yes, hatred, for the psychopathic street punk who had taken Jackie's life. The good one taken, the bad one still with us.

Billy became a cop to get Butch and Anthony and others of their ilk off the streets. He possessed the same instincts as his father, which made him a natural. Unlike his father, he possessed an unerring moral compass, which made him great. Every bust, every conviction of every street thug, provided relief — if only for a moment – from the "what-if" reel. Catch a bad guy. Stop the reel. Rest for a minute. Resume reel. Catch another bad guy. For Billy, the job became a working penance, where every arrest brought him a little bit closer to redemption. Billy became the best kind of cop — sober, honest, dedicated to law and order for his own intensely personal reasons. It was gratifying to put Butch away, but the reel was far from over.

"What else did you get Butch on?"

"He assaulted some gay guys outside of the Barrel House.

Right before he crashed into Jackie."

"He told me he was going to do that," said Brendan. "The night Jackie died. Remember he was at the K with two of his running buddies? Did you get them, too?"

Billy paused. He did not know that Butch had announced his intention to bash gays at the K Tavern before the fatal hit and run. Another "what-if" was added to the reel.

"Yeah. We got them all. My dad got Butch for stealing cars, too."

"Butch was always a triple threat."

"At least."

"What a weapon."

"What a putz."

"Your dad helped to put Butch away?"

"Yeah."

The Alers were well aware of the tension between Billy Ball and his father, both now bullet-headed cops together on the beat in Elizabeth. Both streetwise. Both lethal. But Billy brought a moral purpose to the job that Joe lacked. In fact, Joe was half a wise guy himself, as they well knew.

They did not know that Joe Ball had undergone an on-the-job conversion. When Billy came onto the Elizabeth P.D., Joe took great pains to cover up his many street hustles. To his own surprise, Joe found that he was reluctant to have his son — such an exemplary officer — see the degenerate side of his beat. The coverup became increasingly difficult as Billy learned the streets. Eventually, Joe stopped the hustle and emptied out the criminal deposits from his favor bank. Joe was deeply ashamed of his attempt to pin the Peterstown hit on Jackie.

He joined his son and stood up to Riggi. Joe testified against Anthony Fabrizio and then against Butch Mahon. In time, Joe even gave up his girlfriends on the side. The two now got along well, on the job and off. Billy was anxious for the Alers to understand his father's recent transformation.

"My father broke up the chop shop. The one over on McClellan Street."

Father and son had staked out the chop shop in the North End, raided it and closed it down. The chop shop was owned by Riggi.

"Riggi's being investigated," said Billy. "He's going down."

"What for?"

"Extortion and labor racketeering."

"That's a crime in Elizabeth?" said Brendan.

They all laughed except Billy and Stan, who remained quiet for different reasons.

"What's Meg doing?"

"Got a big promotion," said Billy. "She's running all of dispatch. She's taking criminal justice courses at night. Looking to get a degree."

The image of Meg came into their collective minds – whip smart, exquisite, now college-bound, Meg. Another inward smile at the good turn in her fortunes.

"Her dad got laid off. When Singers closed."

"Stan, maybe you could get him something."

"I'll reach out to her." Stan knew from hard experience that Dunn and Florence preferred to sprinkle their pixie dust on large families, where they might get a multi-generational bang at the ballot box. He was not prepared to burn a favor with the mayor on behalf of the Murphy's and their only child. No call would be made here.

"She's dating Mike Burke," said Billy

"Sounds like she turned cop."

"Hey, I resemble that remark," said Billy.

Knowing laughter. Meg and Mike together. That took some getting used to. In the Aler consciousness, Jackie and Meg would always be a couple, frozen on the shelf like an aging prom photograph. Still, they were happy for her.

Billy, Meg, Mike, and now even Joe Ball, were part of more aggressive policing tactics being deployed against the new violence. With unexpectedly good results. The enforcement of small infractions — broken windows — led to bigger busts that got serial criminals off the streets. Turns out that Joe Ball was right after all: behind every big crime lay a long history of minor ones. Sweat the small stuff and the bigger problems take care of themselves.

Then there was CompStat, which used the new technology to track (and ultimately predict) patterns of crime — a digital version of Joe Ball's criminal almanac. Thus equipped, the cops magnified their presence on the streets and stopped crime before it started. Turns out that Meg was right, too. The Elizabeth P.D. could and did take back the streets.

There were other benefits to the new technology. La Cosa Nostra thrived in the shadows. The new technology included deep surveillance capabilities that shone a bright, disinfectant light on organized crime. The cops and prosecutors would eventually use the new technology – juiced up by the RICO statutes — to take down the bosses.

The mob used unions to control mature industries like construction and transportation. In these slow-moving businesses, loyalty mattered more than competence. The new technology demanded more creativity than obedience, more brains than muscle, more speed than trust. There would be no mobbed up operating systems or hi-speed internet connections. It just wasn't their style. Organized crime would remain behind, locked into the last century.

The Elizabeth P.D. pacified its northern border with Newark and stopped the new violence from spilling over to the North End. Elizabeth did not become the next city occupied by alien federal and state powers. No billionaires descended upon Elizabeth with their overstuffed foundations and self-serving agendas. Elizabeth retained its sovereignty. Mayor Tom Dunn, his machine and his Police Commissioner deserved much of the credit.

But nothing could help Newark, which sank ever deeper into the time-lapsed tragedy of crime, government programs, and poverty. More government money chased out the little private capital that remained in the city – and with it any hope of safety and prosperity. Nothing had improved since the riots of 1967 – and much had gotten worse. The outsiders tried everything. More government buildings. More grants. More non-profits. Always more money. Always more corruption. Newark could — somehow – always manage to avoid deliverance.

The eye of the hurricane passed over the K Tavern. The rain stopped. Bright little rays of sunshine bounced off the sidewalks, the cars, the buildings. For a moment, the humidity dropped. Tiny rainbows popped up everywhere.

The ghost of Jackie Martin broke its drawn gaze and looked around, as if it had just awoken from a dream, suddenly aware of itself and its surroundings. The spirit rose from the stool. It hovered over the Alers for a moment and then floated up to the tin ceiling. The ghost turned to the big picture window and looked out after the passing hurricane.

"How's Benedict's?"

Chris took a breath. Against all odds, St. Benedict's was thriving. Contributions from white alumni, many of whom were not even living in New Jersey anymore, kept the doors open. Enrollment was expanding. After running all their local competitors off the court, the basketball team advanced onto the national stage. Several students of St. Benedict's made it to the NBA. Chris' beloved soccer team ranked number one in the country. In academics, too, St. Benedict's outperformed. Father Ed and his monks sent 98 percent of their graduates to college, often to big-name universities. In time, St. Benedict's would become the inspiration for books, documentaries, and even a fawning Sixty Minutes special.

How to explain the mad, implausible success of St. Benedict's? In the heart of the slow-motion, undying catastrophe that was the city of Newark? Serving the most disadvantaged population in Essex County? For Father Ed and his monks, the answer was simple: follow the ancient Rule of St. Benedict. Stay in place. Love the kids. Repeat.

The archbishop and the men of the Inquisition ceased their efforts to close the school. As always, they had mixed motivations. St. Benedict's shone as an example of Catholic charity and the privileged position of the poor within the Church. The self-sacrifice of the monks glorified the students. The accomplishments of the students glorified the monks. All under the eye of St. Benedict himself, patron and protector, who watched over the school.

The Archbishop also knew a public relations coup when he saw one.

Not everyone was pleased with the success of St. Benedict's. The Black sons of St. Benedict's were not loved for their achievements any more than the white sons were twenty years earlier. Worse, the annoying little organization men of St. Benedict's wore their maroon ties and blazers around the city like the colors of a competing gang. Only this gang studied at night and excelled in extracurricular activities.

The Newark Board of Education did not appreciate the constant and unfavorable comparison to St. Benedict's. How could Father Ed accomplish so much with so little? Why couldn't the Newark school system do a better job, especially with so much money at its disposal? The obvious answer — that a dedicated group of impoverished Catholic monks who offered little more than love and discipline could accomplish greater things than a corrupt secular system with a billion dollar spend — was unacceptable. Every new achievement at St. Benedict's stood as a testament to the talent and drive of the Black community – and an indictment of the welfare state that kept them down. Left to its own devices, St. Benedict's might expand its footprint. The cursed monks might siphon off more students and more state dollars (with a street value of $30,000 a head) from the public system. Ever more kids rescued from poverty and despair. The horror!

The system struck back — with twelve charter and magnet schools within a mile of St. Benedict's – seven within ten blocks. Father Ed could be forgiven for feeling both flattered and threatened. But still St. Benedict's prospered. Enrollment continued to grow. Father Ed opened up a grammar school that doubled as a shelter. In his spare time, he added a new soccer field.

Chris had acquired Father Ed's taste for the impossible. As promised by Father Ed, the crucifix in St. Mary's continued to speak to him. The message remained loud and strong: love the kids, love the kids. Chris spent a good deal of time in St. Mary's, which provided his own stability of place. In time, messages from the crucifix became more real to him than anything out in the secular world.

Chris did not feel he could begin to convey all that had happened to him in the last two years. His former teammates had drifted so far away to such different places. He wasn't sure they could hear him. Even if they could, he didn't think he could articulate the richness and depth of his new spiritual life.

"We're hanging in there."

"How's the doctor?"

"Great. He's on the board of Benedict's. He raises a lot of money for the school."

Chris left it at that.

Two years after Jackie's death, Tom Dunn still ran Elizabeth. He was finally voted out in 1992. But the Dunn Voting Machine Works outlived its founder. Dunn's successor, Chris Bollwage, took over the machine and ran it so well that he was elected for eight consecutive terms as mayor of Elizabeth, eclipsing Tom Dunn's national record. The invisible bond between the mayor and the city electorate endured well into the next century.

Mobsters still swore ancient oaths of fealty in return for protection – at least in the movies. The bright lights of the new technology drove them back into the traditional vice trades. They lost their grip on legitimate businesses. They competed with other gangsters in the drug business, and in the process became more like them. Their code died.

The favor bank continued to thrive in Elizabeth, N.J. Cops kept up their lively trade in services, favors, and obligations – the currency of the blue realm. The shadow system of justice rolled on, providing a flawed foundation for the larger and even more flawed system up in the courthouse. And so, against all odds, the earth continued to spin.

By 1980, one of the seven wonders of Elizabeth had fallen out of the constellation – Singers was gone. The Bayway Refinery, severely wounded by the Colonial Pipeline and automation, continued to shrink its footprint. Employment at the refinery dropped from 15,000 in 1978 to 750 in 2018. By 1985, it no longer qualified as a wonder. Following a long, slow decline under many different owners (a sad saga similar to that of Singers), Burry Biscuits baked its last Scooter Pie on Newark Avenue in 2005. However, the Bayway Exchange was added, reducing the total number of wonders from seven to five. All of the remaining wonders were government agencies. The days of large-scale private manufacturing had come to a close in Elizabeth, N.J.

The Alers moved into the new American service economy as managers, government bureaucrats, movie producers, cops and clergy. No one made a living with his hands. Jackie was the last, a legacy of the once-great industrial base of the city.

The eye of the hurricane passed to the east, pulling along a thin beam of sunshine that fell on the North End. New rain streamed out of the back end of the storm. The gutters filled up again.

The newly awoken ghost of Jackie Martin took one last look at the K Tavern. A slight breeze brushed over the shoulders of the Alers. They looked up as Jackie's ghost slipped out the window onto the tip of the distant hurricane blowing out to sea.

The End.

Made in the USA
Middletown, DE
13 January 2022

58589096R00126